TECUMSEH

Destiny's Warrior

Indian books by David C. Cooke

TECUMSEH: DESTINY'S WARRIOR
FIGHTING INDIANS OF THE WEST
INDIANS ON THE WARPATH
FAMOUS INDIAN TRIBES

TECUMSEH

DESTINY'S WARRIOR

By DAVID C. COOKE

JULIAN MESSNER, INC. • NEW YORK

Published by Julian Messner, Inc.
8 West 40 Street, New York 18

Published simultaneously in Canada
by The Copp Clark Publishing Co. Limited

Printed in the United States of America

Library of Congress Catalog Card No. 59-7011

TO ANN AND ART SUTTON

CONTENTS

TECUMSEH

Destiny's Warrior

1.

SHADOW OF THE LONG KNIVES

The smoke columns talked of war in the bright blue sky of the Ohio country that year. In the haze of early autumn the smoke towered from the signal mounds and word spread among the Shawnee villages that the Long Knives were marching. On an afternoon in September, when the world could offer nothing better to a boy of six than a lesson from a beloved older brother in the art of the bow and arrow, new smoke trailed up to the sky and set the four thousand inhabitants of the Shawnee village of Old Piqua to talking excitedly.

Old Piqua sprawled on the west bank of the Mad River. In the black earth of the river bottoms the Shawnee raised their corn, beans and squash. On the bluff above the bottoms stood the long house, where their tribal sachems gathered when there were matters of importance to be considered. Busy with their lesson in a grove along the bottoms, at first the two boys paid little attention to the smoke and commotion around this house on the bluff.

Then finally the older boy, a youth of sixteen named Cheeseekau, pointed.

"See, Tecumseh!" he said. "Our mother leaves the field with the other women."

The smaller boy raised his head from an arrow he was fitting to the bow. His eyes showed the admiration he held for his older brother who had consented (after much nagging from the little boy) to instruct him.

"What, Cheeseekau? I was not listening."

"There is smoke from the signal mounds to the south, and a great crowd has gathered at the council house." Cheeseekau frowned. "Perhaps more word has come of the Long Knives's army below the Beautiful River. Come, let us find our father." When Cheeseekau snatched his bow and elkskin quiver of arrows from the ground and bolted off through the bottoms along the river's edge, his small brother followed reluctantly. He was too young to be interested in councils, and the Long Knives meant little to him. It seemed more important to his young mind to learn how to use the bow and arrow, so that he could become a great hunter and warrior like his father.

Being only six, Tecumseh knew little of war, except from stories told by the old men. The Ohio lands had drowsed peacefully since Chief Pontiac of the Ottawa made a treaty with the Long Knives. But the small boy began to sense the alarm in the village as the women left their buffalo shoulder plows and turtle shell hoes and hurried up the slope to join the warriors assembling on the bluff.

In the confusion around the council house the boy heard many words which had little meaning to him. As sunset darkened the Mad River, he returned to the wigwam of his father and waited eagerly until the family finished eating the corn meal, wild deer meat and wild rice prepared by Methoataske, his mother, and his gentle-eyed older sister Tecumapease.

Puckeshinwa, the boy's father, a muscular man in spite of his fifty-four summers, said little while eating. Instead, he stared worriedly at the column of smoke rising through the hole at the top of the wigwam.

Tecumseh was about to question his father concerning the smoke talk when Cheeseekau burst into the wigwam. Earlier he had scurried out restlessly without touching more than a few bites of his food. Now he faced Puckeshinwa, eyes glowing.

"Father, is the word true? Cornstalk rides here and will arrive before sundown tomorrow?"

Puckeshinwa nodded. "That is true."

"War with the Long Knives comes, then!" Cheeseekau exclaimed. "And shall I have a chance at last to try my arrows in battle?"

The mother flung her wooden corn mortar and the long grinding pestle angrily on the ground. "Foolish boy! To want war and bloodshed! I have dreamed many dreams of this time, and they have all been very bad. I have feelings that we shall be washed in blood." She turned away sharply.

Puckeshinwa scowled. "Woman, that is false talk to put before the young. The Shawnee fight with honor, and we have always been victorious." Gently he turned to the younger members of the family. "My children, I have taken up the knife many times before, but I tell you one thing: you must always be honorable before your enemy. In that way only can the Shawnee remain an honorable nation. Learn this lesson from me—and remember it."

Methoataske snorted grimly. "Shall the Long Knives heed such fine words?"

"They are honorable men also," Puckeshinwa replied, though his voice sounded doubtful.

Up leaped Cheeseekau again. "I must make my arrowheads sharp!" While the mother looked on gloomily, Puckeshinwa smiled, understanding well his tall son's desire to be tested in combat. When Cheeseekau had gone and Methoataske and Tecumapease were busy putting the last touches on the skin-covered cradle for the coming baby, Tecumseh moved closer to his father's side.

"Why will there be war, Father?"

"Because of a thing called a treaty, a piece of paper signed long ago by Chief Pontiac after he had fought the Long Knives. All the country north of the Ohio River—the Beautiful River—was given to the Shawnee and the other tribes. Now the whites from Virginia have claimed the land as their own, and Lord Dunmore, who is governor, or sachem, of Virginia, has gathered an army and marched into our country. The treaties of the Long Knives, my son, are often empty of the true spirit of a promise . . . that spirit which insures the promise will be kept."

"Why does Cornstalk come here?"

"To gather warriors to meet the Long Knife Dunmore, and throw him back."

"I wish I could go with you to the battle, Father."

With a warm smile the man gripped his son's arm. "Time enough when you grow."

Bending over the U-shaped cradle frame, Methoataske began to sway back and forth and croon to herself—a weird, wordless song which somehow reminded Tecumseh of her words about blood. When he crawled beneath his deerskin blanket that night to sleep, he was strangely afraid.

Magnificent upon his gray pony, face and chest bright with the scarlet paint of war, Cornstalk and a party of twenty braves rode into Old Piqua the next day when the sun stood at the top of the sky. The handsome war chief carried a lance and shield as well as a war club and musket. In the party Tecumseh recognized Blackfish, the stout, good-humored sachem from the Shawnee village of Old Chillicothe to the south. Today Blackfish neither smiled nor appeared to be in good spirits. While the women prepared a feast, the warriors of the village gathered with Cornstalk and Blackfish in the council long house.

All through the afternoon and evening the rich, mighty voice of Cornstalk thundered. It struck a strange chord in Tecumseh's heart. If only one day he might speak as Cornstalk spoke, sit as tall on a pony, carry in his eyes the same strength and wisdom and courage of the mighty war chief. Tecumseh loved his father and knew he was an important man, a chief in the council, but Cornstalk was the war leader of the tribe—someone almost like the Great Spirit, who ruled all the world with his power.

War fires burned at Old Piqua that night.

Tecumseh crept from the wigwam long after his mother had cautioned him to go to sleep. Returning to the council house, where great crowds still waited, he managed to wriggle close and peer through a chink in the logs. He gasped.

Cornstalk stood tall and spoke loudly, and in his bronzed hands, thick with muscle and quick with a tomahawk, he held aloft like some fabulous serpent the great wampum belt, the terrible purple war belt of which Puckeshinwa spoke. The belt stretched nine feet and was splashed bright with vermilion paint, bright as the blood of the Long Knives. Cornstalk passed the war belt, then the pipe. All smoked, and then silently the sachems came from the council house. In the smoke and the firelight of the autumn evening, the word spread across the village—Puckeshinwa had cast his lot with Cornstalk. There would be war against the army of Dunmore.

When Tecumseh finally stole back to the wigwam to dream of battle, Old Piqua resounded with the music of wooden flutes and drums, and the shrill cries of the war dance. The drums thudded, the voices grew more frenzied as the dancers leaped in the ancient ritual of battle. At last, Tecumseh thought, he had seen an image of what he wanted to become . . . a warrior as great as Cornstalk, whose eye was lightning, whose voice rolled like the thunder before the spring rains . . . thunder which made every other chief listen and nod agreement.

When Cornstalk left the following day the village fell into a rush of preparation for the coming battle. Cheeseekau was overjoyed when he learned he would be allowed to accompany the braves. Puckeshinwa, however, fell into gloomy spells and appeared unhappy a great deal of the time. Tecumseh thought often of his father's sadness, and one evening when no one else was in the wigwam, he asked him about it.

Puckeshinwa shook his head. "On the night we learned of Cornstalk's coming, your mother spoke strange words. She is a good woman, my son, but her dreams are troubled. Often she sees things the rest of us cannot see. I have thought much of her words that night, and I feel very strongly that when I ride with Cornstalk I shall never come back to this town which I love so well."

Tecumseh seized his father's hand. "You will come back to us! I know it."

"There has been peace for many summers," his father continued. "I begin to believe with your mother that the war will not be an honorable one, but one in which the Shawnee and all the tribes shall fight like animals who are helpless against the powers of the great hunter." Suddenly he fixed the boy with his warm, kindly gaze. "Make me the promise which my other children have made."

"I will, Father."

"To carry the knife and the bow with honor, to be brave, but to be generous and kind as well. Always remember that an enemy is also a man, who laughs and cries just as you do."

Tecumseh nodded slowly, more disturbed than ever by his father's strange thoughts.

In the month of October, 1774, Cornstalk moved across the Ohio country as fall crimsoned the leaves and put a tang of winter in the air. In his army were warriors of the Mingo tribe, the Delaware, the Wyandot and the Shawnee. Puckeshinwa had gone from Old Piqua with a large force of braves, and he joined the Shawnee chiefs—Cornstalk, Blue Jacket, Red Eagle and

Logan—as they marched south toward the Ohio . . . the Beautiful River. Daily the smoke columns carried the word from signal mound to signal mound.

Tecumseh became listless and unhappy as news of the fate of the army suddenly stopped. His mother took to singing her weird songs more often, waking in the middle of the dark night shrieking of strange monsters in her dreams. Old Piqua waited, and none waited with heavier heart than Tecumseh.

On the tenth day of October, at Point Pleasant in West Virginia, Cornstalk's army was driven from the battlefield in defeat by Dunmore's soldiers commanded by General Andrew Lewis. Tecumseh learned of this when the Shawnee party straggled back into Old Piqua weeks later. Still . . . there . . . down the line of warriors were Puckeshinwa and Cheeseekau! Both had come home! Tecumseh ran forward, broke from the crowd welcoming the braves, clasped his father's legs and hugged him. All the strange warnings—the terrible dreams and fears—had been foolish. Puckeshinwa's face bore the frown of the saddened soldier who had lost the battle, but he was alive.

He explained that Cornstalk, fearing attacks on his people during the coming winter, had signed another paper called the Treaty of Camp Charlotte. No longer could the Shawnee use the Kentucky lands below the Ohio for their hunting grounds; the treaty had given that land to the Long Knives, who promised to live in peace with Cornstalk's people. The march of the whites into the Shawnee country north of the river had stopped, at least for a time.

Winter fell soon after. The fires burned bright and happy in the wigwam of Puckeshinwa. There were family games . . . dice for the older children, brightly painted wooden tops for the younger. Gone were the fears . . . until the snowy winter afternoon when Puckeshinwa did not come back from the forest in the gray twilight.

Tecumseh wakened at dawn next day to find his mother putting a heavy buffalo robe over her blouse and wrap-around skirt of deerskin. As he sat up, she put a finger to her lips.

"Do not wake the others. Your father has not returned. He promised to be gone but one day hunting—and a night has passed. I am going into the forest to search."

"Let me go with you!" Tecumseh said, throwing aside his own sleeping robe.

Through the wailing forest, whipped by the wind, long sheets of snow attacked the face, numbed the lips, crusted the eyes with frost. Tecumseh clung to his mother's side, stamping along on his small snowshoes through thick drifts on the familiar hunting trail which ran along the river's shore south of the village. They searched for several hours. At last, while Tecumseh was pulling himself, shivering, from a snowbank into which he had stumbled, he heard the scream of his mother, keening above the wind from up the trail:

"Ai-eeeeee!"

Fear and horror drove Tecumseh quickly through the snow . . . and on a low bank leading down to the frozen river lay an ice-crusted thing that appeared to be a man. On all sides the snow was red with great patches of fresh blood.

"Who . . . who . . . ?" Tecumseh tried to call over the wind.

Methoataske put aside her snowshoes, dropped to her knees and brushed ice crystals from her husband's face. His eyes fluttered open dully. New blood stained the snow as she tried to move him. He had been shot by a musket ball. While Methoataske rubbed his frozen face, Tecumseh knelt on the other side of his father, too frightened to let a single tear come from his eyes. The wind through the forest turned the world to a terrifying nightmare of white and gray. Methoataske put her mouth close to Puckeshinwa's ear.

"Who did this foul thing, my husband?"

"White . . . white men." Puckeshinwa coughed terribly and gasped out the story.

He had been delayed by the snow in returning to the village. Then, just after dawn that morning, three Long Knives, wearing beaded deerskin clothing and carrying muskets, had come across the river on the ice. They hailed him and asked him to guide their hunting. Puckeshinwa had refused, since he was ready to return to his village, and two of the Long Knives had turned on him with muskets and shot him. All three had gone off somewhere beyond the white curtain of the snow.

"We shall take you to the village," Methoataske declared. "Come, try to rise."

"I cannot!"

"You must try!"

While Tecumseh struggled to help, his mother dragged the heavy man to his knees. Then she cried out sharply as Puckeshinwa toppled forward, limp. Tecumseh's will broke and he sobbed, throwing himself on his father's body. Methoataske seized her son's shoulders and jerked him to his feet, a terrible anger whipping her features into an ugly pattern.

"You heard who killed this good man!" she cried above the wind. "Long Knives! Not honorable men as your father said, but butchers. I will make you swear to kill the Long Knives when you are grown tall! You shall bring vengeance for this crime, and your name shall be known because you are the avenger. You shall think only one thought—that you must kill the Long Knives who did this terrible thing. Swear now!" Driven almost out of her senses, she shook her son. "Swear, now! Swear now, Tecumseh! *Swear to avenge!*"

Seeing the bloody snow, the face frozen and rimmed with icy death in the middle of a desolate white wilderness, Tecumseh raised his eyes to the snow-swept heaven and said, "I swear."

And in his heart he meant the oath as he had never meant anything before.

Together, the boy and his mother pulled the body back toward Old Piqua. And while the world was made dead by winter, Puckeshinwa was put into the ground for his final rest, on the frozen banks of the Mad River.

2. THE TRICKS OF BROTHER BOONE

In the Shawnee tongue the name Tecumseh stands for "I Cross Someone's Path." The young boy hardly realized how much the name meant when, early in 1775, his mother went to the female segregation house and returned with the child she had been carrying at the time of her husband's murder. In the wigwam now squalled the last offspring of Puckeshinwa, a rather sickly boy named Laulewasika. Tecumseh had little interest in the new child, yet their paths were crossed from the moment of birth as surely as two vines climb together in the forest toward the sun, and cannot grow apart because they are linked by destiny in hundreds of turns and twists.

Methoataske paid little attention to the child. Her husband's murder had driven her to even longer and stranger silences. The lost, sad gleam of her eye and her peculiar songs upset young Tecumseh and the other children for a time. Then, slowly, he began to realize that his mother was not like other women of the tribe . . . that she no longer acted as his mother, but was simply a woman who dwelt in the wigwam and left the care of the children to the gentle older sister Tecumapease.

As Tecumseh grew through his seventh and eighth years, he became more accustomed to having a mother who was no mother. Peace had come again to the Ohio land, and there was much to occupy the lively mind and body of a growing Shawnee boy who already showed signs of becoming a tall, handsome warrior. Tecumseh learned to work with his hands—to carve and fashion a bow from a single piece of wood, to construct the light birch canoes which carried the Shawnee on the Mad River, to fish with small nets woven of strips of skin. Elders took the young boys into their cabins and taught them the history of the tribe—the legends of the old grandmother Skemotah who lived somewhere in the sky and was forever nimbly weaving a mighty net into which all good Shawnee would be taken to the happy hunting grounds at death. Cheeseekau, too, was a good teacher, and the lessons with bow and tomahawk became more serious, for Tecumseh learned quickly. And during a lazy summer not long after Puckeshinwa's burial, Tecumseh found a second father.

He had ventured alone on a hunting trip close to the Shawnee village of Old Chillicothe, to the south of Old Piqua. At nightfall, in a sudden rainstorm, he quickly decided to make for Old Chillicothe since it lay close at hand. Certainly some family would take him in for the night.

Luck went with him through the rain, for he found himself in the wigwam of the most important man in Old Chillicothe—Blackfish, sachem of the town. Over a crackling fire, while Tecumseh ate corn meal from a bowl with a wooden spoon, the stout, good-natured chief surveyed the boy approvingly.

"Puckeshinwa would have been proud of you," he said. "It saddens me to think he is not among us to see what his fine black-haired offspring has become. I have heard tales, Tecumseh, saying you can throw the tomahawk as far as your brothers Cheeseekau and Sauwaseekau, who are close to manhood now, and that when you are taught the history of the tribe, you are the cleverest pupil at Old Piqua."

Tecumseh said nothing, for it was not his place to comment. Blackfish sighed.

"You look much like my own son. He was killed two summers ago in Kentucky, by hunters under Boone, the Long Knife."

"Boone?" Tecumseh perked up. "That name I have heard often. Who is Boone?"

"Dan-i-el Boone," Blackfish replied, "is the cleverest fox of all the Long Knives. He slips like a ghost through the woods, and has killed many Shawnee and Mingo." Then he added swiftly, "But he killed my son in an honorable battle, and the Shawnee might do very well to have many men as clever in the forest as Boone." Abruptly Blackfish brightened as an idea lighted his face.

"Tecumseh, you are alone now, and I am alone. Puckeshinwa is dead, and I hear that your mother sings strange songs, that she dreams much and does not tend the family."

"That is so," Tecumseh answered sadly.

"Then you shall be my son!" Blackfish exclaimed. "I shall adopt you as mine!"

Tecumseh glanced up, filled with excitement. Of all the Shawnee sachems to have for a father, Blackfish would be best. "I . . . I would like to become the son of my father Blackfish."

The older man clapped the boy warmly on the shoulder. "It shall be done tomorrow, then."

Thus in official ceremony did Tecumseh wash and purify himself and become in truth the son of Blackfish. As he grew, he ran many times over the trail between Old Piqua and Old Chillicothe, a bronzed figure in soft-soled moccasins and breech-cloth. He spent at least half of his time in Blackfish's town. The heavy, good-humored chief and his thin wife welcomed him into their childless wigwam, and Tecumseh found Blackfish a better teacher even than Cheeseekau. Together the man and the boy roamed the forests, hunting and tracking.

"Here," Blackfish would say, "let us imagine we are six Shawnee, and up there, behind that growth of wild plum, are twelve Long Knives. We must fight. Let us plot how we would attack. You shall be the leader."

Tecumseh squatted on the carpet of dead leaves and grass, a buffalo robe wrapped over his leggings and skin shirt, and said, "Through that opening, my father, between the elm and the hawthorn bushes, I would send three of my warriors."

Blackfish shook his head. "No. For—see—beyond the hawthorns there is a clearing, and the Long Knives could fire down upon your braves." He pointed in the opposite direction. "There! *That* narrow trail. Creep up behind! Surprise them!"

Tecumseh was an eager student, for he still raged with the fire of hatred kindled by the murder of his father. In his mind all white men were objects of suspicion. They would slay you if given a chance, and when they signed a name to one of their treaty papers, or extended the pipe in friendship, they seldom could be depended upon to fulfill the agreement or preserve the friendship. Tecumseh thought often about the treachery of the whites, and his beliefs were reinforced in the fall of 1777. He was nearly ten years old, sturdy and black haired, when a cry went up along the trail from the south. A panting runner threw himself at the feet of Blackfish.

"Cornstalk is dead! And his son Ellinipsico—and three more."

"How did this happen?" Blackfish demanded, his face growing dark.

"Cornstalk died with the musket balls of the Long Knives in his body."

Blackfish scowled grimly and motioned. "Sit at my side and tell the story."

The runner reported that Cornstalk had visited Fort Randolph, which stood at Point Pleasant in West Virginia, scene of his defeat a few years earlier. At this fort were gathered the Long Knife Americans who even now were fighting a great war with the soldiers of the great British king, George III, across the big water. Cornstalk had declared that the Ohio tribes would take no sides in this revolutionary war, but in the late summer of 1777 he had journeyed to Fort Randolph to warn the Long Knives that scattered villages among the Ohio tribes were thinking of helping the soldiers of the British. The Long Knives had persuaded the chief to stay at the fort and help them draw maps of the Ohio country.

"Only a few days ago," the runner said, "Gilmore, a Long Knife hunter, was killed along the Beautiful River by tribesmen we do not know. Since Cornstalk's son Ellinipsico had been away from the fort of the Long Knives, they said he had killed Gilmore. An angry mob of soldiers marched against Cornstalk's cabin. He would not fight because he said his son had not done the murder. Though Cornstalk spoke the truth, the white soldiers shot him seven times, then shot his son and three others as well. All are dead. I have carried this word through all the towns, for the crime is a terrible one."

Blackfish drew his tomahawk, raised his arm and flung the weapon to the ground. It bit the earth with a wicked sound.

"The whites will not believe the truth even when it is spoken. And did they not promise to be brothers to Cornstalk? I shall call the chiefs together. The Long Knives shall be paid for these murders."

In the early winter, Blackfish and his warriors marched to the Ohio River to strike at the Kentucky towns. Tecumseh heard little of their progress. April came, bringing green to the land once more, when a commotion went up in Old Chillicothe, for Blackfish and his party were returning. A small army of braves straggled into the village, and Tecumseh, leaving off a lively game of hoop-and-pole with some of the other boys, ran to watch the returning procession. Beside Blackfish rode a lanky white man in buckskin, a twined sash, a cap of coonskin with a coon's tail dangling behind his head. The lean, tanned Yankee surveyed the Shawnee, smiling lazily when a bare-bottomed tot clad only in a quillwork headband ran across the path. Blackfish talked with the Long Knife as they rode along.

"Who is that?" Tecumseh asked, tugging at the arm of a youth near him.

"They are saying the name Boone."

"Boone!" Tecumseh drew back a step, for the name spelled terror to most of the tribes along the frontier.

That evening in the wigwam Tecumseh found Daniel Boone no fire-eyed monster, but a slow, even-tempered white man of more than forty summers, who squatted by the meal fire as though he had been doing it all of his life, and consumed gobbets of deer meat with as much relish as Blackfish himself. The chief beamed happily, looking on the famed hunter as a kind of new plaything. Outside the wigwam buzzed the voices of the curious. Tecumseh felt lucky to be so close to the great Long Knife, and especially so when Blackfish presented him to Boone.

"I am pleased to know you, Tecumseh," Boone spoke in fluent Shawnee. "It's lucky we got captured, eh, Blackfish? In Kaintuck the food's not nearly so good."

"We fell upon the mighty Boone while he was hunting," Blackfish explained to the boy. "We have been to the fort of the British in Detroit."

"That's true," Boone assented. "My boys and I stole out of Boonesborough on New Year's day, bent for the Licking River Springs. Kaintuck forts and stations were crying for salt, so off we went with some kettles given to me by old Patrick Henry himself. We boiled and boiled, eight hundred and forty gallon of water for one bushel of salt, and my boys were still boiling away when I went out after a few buffalo." He grinned. "That's when Blackfish sneaked up on me. I should remember that's the way you Shawnee fight. I saw he had plenty braves along, so I talked my boys into giving up with their scalps still attached." He wiped his greasy mouth with his buckskin sleeve. "So off we went to Detroit, where your father here traded all my boys except me for a hundred dollars in goods per head."

Leaning back on his elbows, Boone finished, "Me, I'm satisfied where I am."

"Tomorrow," Blackfish declared, "you shall be adopted."

Boone picked his teeth. "Suits me all right." He glanced at Tecumseh with a sly grin, "Hello, little brother."

With a gulp and a nod, Tecumseh fled from the wigwam to spread the astonishing news among his friends. Boone appeared quite content to be a prisoner of the tribes, yet Tecumseh had seen a sly glint of humor in his eyes several times in the wigwam, as if, like a fox, he played a trick. Delighted with his capture, Blackfish apparently did not notice this flash of cunning.

When the sun broke over the green horizon in the morning, the whole village descended to the river for the cermony. Boone was stripped of his clothes and pushed into the water and scrubbed so hard that his skin shone pinkly raw, and he shouted several times in English, "*Oww!* Holt off there a bit!" Then his long hair was cut to a scalp lock, his body daubed with paint, and the ceremony conducted at the council house, with much talk and passing of the feather-decorated red stone pipe.

The tribes of the Ohio needed every possible hand to carry on the daily work of the village, and so the practice of adoption of whites had become common. Boone had his own wigwam and was even allowed to carry his own wicked-looking scalp knife. Dressing for warming weather as any brave of the tribe, in breechcloth, hunting shirt, leggings and beaded moccasins with cuffs, he went on hunting forays into the forest with parties of warriors, gathering food for the tribes. April passed and became May. Tecumseh hovered near Boone's wigwam in the evenings, when the Long Knife would sit alone and smoke a clay pipe as the sun burned low and red like an eye above the river. They talked of war, and especially of the blade—originally a sword but now a hunting knife—for which the Long Knives had been named.

"You're a bright boy, Tecumseh. Ten summers, are you?"

"That is true, my brother."

"Done much with a knife like this?" Boone juggled the blade with its point on the ball of one finger. "It's a handy instrument. Say you land in trouble as I did, and you hand across your tomahawk—here, you take my tomahawk."

Tecumseh stepped forward and extended his right hand to seize the imaginary weapon from Boone's right hand.

"Now then," Boone chuckled, the sly fox glint in his eye again, "all I need do is let the tomahawk drop and with my hand—" Whiplash quick he gripped Tecumseh's throat. His left hand traced the point of the knife across the boy's belly, without injuring the flesh. While Tecumseh scowled unhappily over the trick played upon him, Boone leaned back and laughed. "See there, Tecumseh? Your enemy is dead with his gizzard bleeding and you are alive to tell about it."

"Tricks do not belong in a war between honorable men," Tecumseh said, a bit doubtfully. "You had surrendered."

Boone gaped and said in English, "You ain't serious?" Then he translated his astonishment.

Tecumseh nodded stiffly. "So my father Puckeshinwa taught me. He also taught me to help my enemies if they are hurt and can do me no harm."

"Why, boy, the only way to fight any kind of battle is with every trick you know. Upset them, confuse them, put them running in circles—but win. Win! Don't stop till they're dead. That's the way it has to be out here in this wilderness, because the whites want to keep living."

"Is that how the Long Knives make war?" Tecumseh asked. "The same way they make promises and write treaty papers—with tricks?

"Why not? Common sense, that's all."

Tecumseh felt stiff and uncomfortable. "My way is not the way of the Long Knives, then," he declared.

"Well, I doubt whether you will keep your scalp in place very long thinking that way," Boone said slowly.

"If you use tricks," Tecumseh argued, "why have you not used them to escape from our village? Look at your hands. They are not tied!"

Boone puffed his pipe, and the sunset put red gleams in his eyes. "Why, boy," he said, grinning crookedly, "I'm happy here. I don't want to escape; I enjoy this life."

Tecumseh did not believe it. But later that same night he pondered Boone's words about making war, and he realized the white man had spoken the truth. The Long Knives did not fight honorably as the Shawnee did. The way they had murdered Cornstalk, after he had signed a peace treaty, proved that.

Full summer came to the Mad River country with the month of June. Word circulated in Old Chillicothe that Blackfish planned a raid south of the Beautiful River on Boonesborough, Kentucky. Tecumseh saw a hunting party return on a sunlit afternoon minus one member—Boone. It seemed Boone had told the leader of the party about spotting a particularly choice hunting area—and in the middle of a bramble thicket had fled, stolen a horse and ridden south through the forest.

In August, when Blackfish and his warriors marched out of Old Chillicothe, Tecumseh had his doubts about the success of the campaign. Boone's escape was timed too closely with the news of the attack on the Kentucky settlement. And sure enough, Tecumseh's fears were realized. Blackfish returned to

Old Chillicothe, the ten-day siege of Boonesborough a failure. Warned by Boone, the whites there had been prepared.

"Trickery defeated us," Blackfish declared to his adopted son. Tecumseh doubted, but said nothing. In his forest war and hunting lessons from Blackfish, Tecumseh had been exposed early to the Shawnee's main battle tactic—the surprise attack. Though the tribal hunters took considerably more care when stalking animals, being careful to estimate wind direction and the quarry's sense of smell, when it came to organized battle they seemed unable to devise any strategy except stealth—creeping up on the foe and then rushing in large numbers.

Thinking about it, Tecumseh had decided that there must be other methods of making war—methods which could be successful, clever and honorable as well. Surely the flaws in the Shawnee strategy were apparent, Tecumseh reasoned, considering that the attack on Boonesborough had failed only because Boone had delivered a warning and had robbed the Shawnee of surprise.

Yet Tecumseh knew that the Long Knives won battles even when their enemies knew of their coming long hours ahead. It would not be wise for a boy of his age to question Blackfish, yet he resolved to explore other methods when he became a warrior and led his own army to take vengeance on the Long Knives.

3. THE DAY OF THE BURNING

All across the green frontier of the new American continent the tribes settled once more into uneasy quiet. Blackfish regained a portion of his humor after the unsuccessful march, but he spoke often of the fighting which would certainly come again. Even though Cornstalk's treaty had given the whites the hunting grounds below the Ohio, it was clear that they had an insatiable appetite for more land. They took a piece here, a piece there, waited a time and then simply moved into territory not covered by treaties. Whenever they canceled a treaty, they enforced the cancellation by armed force.

By now Tecumseh's mother scarcely spoke any more, and when she did, she crooned wild and frightening warnings which still disturbed the boy deeply, though he had become accustomed to them. His gentle sister Tecumapease took care of all the children, including four-year-old Laulewasika, who showed signs of being as moody as his mother.

Coming into the wigwam one hot afternoon, Tecumseh found his small brother idly using a piece of twine to play cat's cradle with Tecumapease.

"Have you no heart for the outdoors, Laulewasika?" he said, touching the boy's head. "The sun is warm and the muskellunge are dancing in the brook. Come and watch me plant my spear in one of the big fish in the water, and then snare him in my net!"

Stubbornly Laulewasika shook his head. "I do not want to go with you," he piped in his child's voice. "I like the shadows here."

Tecumseh glanced helplessly at Tecumapease.

"What ails him, sister? He never wishes to be in the sun, or do any of the things we liked when we were as little as he."

Giving a disturbed frown, Tecumapease shook her head. "Little Laulewasika seems much like. . ."

Suddenly the girl halted in her speech, flushing deeply. Tecumseh nodded.

Like all Shawnee, Tecumapease believed in respecting the elders. Yet Tecumseh knew what she had been about to say, and he could not help but agree: Laulewasika, at four, already showed traces of the peculiar behavior which made their mother so shunned by the others of the tribe. The little boy's loneliness made a sorrowful feeling rise in his heart. He did not like to see anyone sorrowing, being lonely or in pain.

"Go away," Laulewasika muttered with a childish lisp. He peered dreamily at the twine wrapped around his finger. "Go away and leave me here alone."

Eleven-year-old Tecumseh went unhappily from the wigwam. He soon heard the hoots and cries signaling the start of a game at the edge of the village. His moccasined feet thudded in the dusk as he raced between cabins and onto the sloping, grassy areas where close to a hundred young Shawnee had gathered. Two peeled saplings had been thrust into the ground six feet apart at each end of the long field, and the boys of the tribe ranged themselves at one extreme, the girls at the other. Someone tossed a ball of hides into the air, and with shrill giggles and shouts the primitive football game was underway.

Tecumseh raced as the ball bounced aloft and the players grappled for it. In the hot sun his muscles worked smoothly. At one point he shouted sharply for the game to stop while he lent a hand to one of the girls, who had stepped into a hole hidden by grass and twisted her leg. When he made sure that she was not seriously hurt, he called for the game to resume. The girl flashed a smile at him. Suddenly he felt an inward sense of pride and warmth—there was a good feeling inside when a moment was taken to help someone less fortunate.

And, at the same time, Tecumseh had grown suddenly conscious of the way his voice, lifted in quick command, had brought the game to a stop. More and more he found that the children his age—and even those older—listened attentively to his ideas. This, too, was pleasing, though it was also a bit frightening to know that he could influence others to do what he wished. It made a proper choice even more necessary.

As the game wore on the girls found themselves somewhat outplayed by the boys, so that the score stood at four goals to six. Then suddenly a chorus of hoarse, excited shouting rose from the village.

Tecumseh turned, shielded his eyes, then shouted, "Hush! Stop the chattering and see!"

"Look, they are running to the council house!" a girl exclaimed.

Such activity in the village spelled only one thing—serious trouble. The hide ball was abandoned in the deep grass, the rivalry forgotten; a hundred youngsters descended into the village at a run. Around the council house all was a babble of noise. Tecumseh located Cheeseekau and Sauwaseekau, who were entering the council house to sit with the elders.

"My brothers, what has happened?"

"A runner tells us the Long Kinves have attacked Old Chillicothe," Sauwaseekau said.

In an agony of suspense, Tecumseh waited while the sun dropped low over the Mad River. At last the men emerged. No one laughed. No one spoke. A strange pall of silence fell on the town. Tecumseh dogged his older brothers' heels all the way back to the wigwam, not wishing to disturb their angry silence. Cheeseekau halted, drove a fist into the palm of his hand and grunted.

"There will be war again."

Tecumseh moved forward, scuffing a toe in the dust. Sauwaseekau slipped an arm around his young brother's shoulder. "Blackfish is well," he said. "The troops of the Long Knives, commanded by the Colonel John Bowman from Kentucky, were beaten back. They marched to the river to the south. They attacked because some scattered Shawnee have spied and scouted for the red-coated soldiers of the British king. Only a few Shawnee were killed."

"How many Long Knife soldiers?" Tecumseh asked.

"Three hundred," Cheeseekau said. "Blackfish fought from the council house, after a dog barked and gave the alarm. Bowman believed he would find your father sleeping, but the animal's noise aroused a woman, who cried 'Kaintuck!' " Cheeseekau smiled grimly. "That council house is hickory log, my brother. Sixty feet square, and it was packed with braves. Bowman mistakenly divided his forces—and lost. But the very defeat means great danger. Once beaten, the Long Knives will return. Although they are busy in their war with the great British king, they will find time to give us back the sword for defeating them."

Shortly after sundown, a party of over four hundred men, women and children gathered, together with their ponies and all their goods. The leader Shinwaskee, a sour-faced old subchief, declared loudly that he was taking his followers to a place of refuge.

"Stay in Old Piqua and suffer the wrath of the Long Knives!" he cried. "Today we have received a warning, and all who are wise will heed it swiftly."

A horse neighed. Someone held a flickering torch high, and at the edge of the crowd Tecumseh saw a familiar face. Dazed, he looked again. Standing among the women was Methoataske, snowshoes and a large beaded pouch strapped to her back. Tecumseh darted forward as the large caravan began to move from the village. Relatives wailed. The firelight threw dancing shadows, and unhappiness was in the darkness as Shinwaskee raised his arm and cantered his pony forward toward the river bottoms.

"My mother!" Tecumseh cried, seizing her arm. "Where are you going?"

She hardly seemed to recognize him. "To the West," she replied absently. "To the land which will be free of the blood that is sure to run in Old Piqua now that Blackfish has turned back the white soldiers." Her strange dark eyes swept the torchlit village. "Fools! Fools to stay here and feel the bite of the knife!" With an odd, sad laugh she lurched forward through the crowd and was lost as the other women picked up their burdens. Shinwaskee was galloping into the bottoms now.

As the moon rose, Tecumseh watched the frightened procession churning the Mad River, sending up spurts of foam and silver-flecked water. Horses whinnied; voices chanted a mournful wordless song. The final straggler disappeared into the silver woods west of the river.

Tecumseh turned, biting his lips, and plunged toward his wigwam. There he flung himself on a deerskin and sobbed without control. Tecumapease laid a cool hand on his forehead but said nothing. Dreamy eyed, the child Laulewasika dropped shiny stones in a bowl made of gray pottery. Cheeseekau stood grimly, silently, arms crossed, in the guttering light of the fire, the other children clustered around him.

Humiliated, Tecumseh rose after a moment and wiped angrily at his cheeks.

"Why did she go?" he blurted. His anguished eyes appealed to the gentle older sister. "Why was she made sick and strange, so that she must follow the cowardly Shinwaskee?"

Tecumapease replied, "We must take pity on her wounded mind, little brother. When Puckeshinwa died. . ."

Silence. A twig popped in the fire. Cheeseekau nodded.

"Yet she spoke truth. There will be blood."

"Hush!" Tecumapease chided, holding Tecumseh close. "We shall manage together."

Slowly Tecumseh forced a smile to his face. This must be part of growing up . . . this terrible hollow pain his mother's departure had started, deep inside him. To be a man, to carry the new responsibilities that would now be thrust on all the male children in the family, he must mask the inward ache, must live from each day to the next as though he did not feel the pain at all. In the firelight the eleven-year-old boy suddenly felt that he had glimpsed a bit of what it meant to be truly grown to manhood. The growing, he learned that night, would not be easy.

One year later, in 1780, the war drums were rolling again across Ohio.

The Army of the West, commanded by George Rogers Clark, who had captured Vincennes in the Indiana lands from the British, massed an army on the Licking River. The smoke columns towered tall in the summer sky, carrying the message from hilltop to hilltop from the Beautiful River to Old Chillicothe and Old Piqua. On the twentieth of July came word that Kentucky volunteers, still outraged by their defeat at the hands of Blackfish, rallied round Clark. Seven hundred Long Knives crossed the Beautiful River north into the fertile land of the Shawnee. Horses dragged a dreaded six-pound cannon ready to scatter leaden destruction among the tribes.

Tecumseh was engaged in a mock battle with a group of

youths in the woods near the bottoms when one of them cried out and pointed.

From the forest poured the inhabitants of Old Chillicothe, Blackfish riding ahead at a gallop. Instantly, the mock battle forgotten, Tecumseh raced up the hill. Blackfish alighted grimly, his body stained with paint and sweaty streaks of dirt. The gathering crowd cried for news. Blackfish raised both arms and shouted.

"The Long Knife Clark comes! We fired Old Chillicothe."

"What?"

"To the torch?"

"Burned Old Chillicothe?"

Wiping sweat from his face, Blackfish roared: "We could not have stopped the Long Knives there! We burned the town so that they would come after us. For here we must make our stand." And quickly Blackfish began to issue orders. Tecumseh stood on the sidelines, excited by the prospect of battle. This time, he knew, Blackfish and the Shawnee would surely be triumphant!

The eighth of August dawned.

Runners came into the village; yes, Clark's army approached. It would reach Old Piqua before noon. Blackfish ordered a hasty evacuation of the women and children.

"Cheeseekau! Sauwaseekau!" Tecumseh pleaded with his brothers. "Let me fight beside you!"

"Into the forest!" Cheeseekau replied sternly. Daubed with paint, hefting war shields and bows, deerskin quivers of arrows on their backs, the brothers were in no mood to argue. The braves were already racing into the corn bottoms where Blackfish planned to stand and fight. Before Tecumseh could protest Cheeseekau cuffed him lightly and pushed him after Tecumapease, already hurrying with the other women and dragging the younger children behind. Disappointed, Tecumseh followed. A shrill cry went up. A shot rang out in the forest somewhere. Tecumseh scuttled after his sister. The village became a dead, haunted place where a light breeze blew in the hot noon sun, fluttering a forgotten feather-decked lance.

Shortly before noon George Rogers Clark and his seven hundred men struck.

Mounted troops charged across the river bottoms where the Shawnee were waiting. The Mad River rang with musket fire and the shrill cries of Indians, who fought desperately. Clark brought up his six-pounder. The fuse was lit on the bluff. Systematic shelling of the bottoms began. The Shawnee fought with bow and arrow, the whites with muskets. Buckskin-garbed frontiersmen and Shawnee clung together in desperate hand-to-hand struggle where the corn grew tall and ripe in the black earth along the river.

Tecumseh watched from a clump of trees, having slipped away from the rest of the family. As the afternoon darkened and the battle continued, the Shawnee slowly gave ground. Great chunks of metal flew through the air when the six-pounder spoke. The Shawnee with their arrows were no match for Clark, his cannon and his muskets and his cavalry. By the time darkness came, without a moon, the forest whispered with the feet of the retreating braves. Now and again a voice, sometimes that of Blackfish, called orders. The forest was alive with running men. Tecumseh rose at last, shocked, sickened that Blackfish had been defeated.

Only a few shots cut the night air. Tecumseh ran in the direction of the retreating Shawnee army. He saw the heavens light and turn angry red. Clark was putting Old Piqua to the torch! When Tecumseh rejoined his people scattered through several clearings above the town, he remained awake all night huddled close to Tecumapease. All watched the red, burning heavens. Old women cried and wailed.

In the morning, long wisps of smoke still stained the sky.

The forest lay silent except for the cheeping of birds and the whisper of the river. The Long Knives had gone back to the Ohio, marching as swiftly as they had come. Slowly the Shawnee crawled from their hiding places, and with Blackfish leading they began the weary return to the village.

For three miles the black, fertile river bottoms smoldered. Every last stalk of corn had been cut, trampled and put to the torch.

The vegetable gardens had been trodden under the hoofs of horses.

Every building in the town had been fired.

Here and there among the corpses a Shawnee still lived, crying out in unbearable agony.

The whole earth crawled with smoke and smelled of death for three long miles along the river.

Tecumapease walked into the village, Tecumseh at her heels. Cheeseekau sifted through the ashes where their wigwam had stood. Sharp cries went up frequently as someone discovered a son, a husband, a loved one among the dead. The very earth was hot, hot as hatred against the soles of Tecumseh's feet. Cheeseekau found the corpse of a warrior who had been a special friend. He vanished somewhere beyond a ruined patch of succotash beans, horribly ill. The hatred rose within Tecumseh so violent and acid that it was as though he had drunk the firewater of the Long Knives, which made a man's head burn and his thoughts whirl and his mind lose all its sense.

On her knees, Tecumapease cried. Laulewasika poked about in the ashes with a strange, indifferent look on his little face.

As the morning wore on, groups were organized to search the surrounding river bottoms for the tribal dead. Tecumseh found himself the center of a group of boys his age and older, and instinctively they turned to him for instruction. He forced his voice to sound clearly and unshaken as he sent his group in twos and threes in various directions.

Searching through the charred fields, Tecumseh thought suddenly that the new lessons of manhood were coming to him swiftly—and painfully. In this battle, he had felt sure Blackfish and his warriors would emerge victorious since their cause was just. Perhaps the victory did not always go to those in the right. Perhaps it took more than idealism to defeat the power of the unjust. Perhaps it also took wisdom, the planning of a mind educated as completely as the mind of the enemy. . .

When Tecumseh's band returned to the village with the body of a slain warrior, they saw Blackfish approaching through the seared wreckage.

"Come, come." He gathered small groups of people about him. "Come, come, cease your crying. We must bury the dead and find a new home." Tiredly he went from ruined wigwam to ruined wigwam. "Cease your crying. We must move from here to a new home."

Tecumseh faced him, white with young anger.

"This is not honorable war, my father. This is foul. Long Knife Clark did not need to burn. . ."

Blackfish nodded, extremely tired. His stomach sagged. "No. He did not need to burn."

"My father. My mother. My village. I shall hate the Long Knives greatly—and kill them." Before Blackfish could control the youth, he was shouting, letting loose all the pent-up emotions stored in his mind: "Kill them, *kill them*!"

Through the night the funeral songs rose wailing to the Ohio sky. Tecumseh helped with the burial of the dead. At last the survivors banded together and left their ruined home. Tecumseh had but one wish: that his own name should someday bring terrible fear to the Long Knives and strike the same terror which the name Clark had struck in the hearts of the Shawnee.

More than ever, now, he swore there would be vengeance. But he had learned a lesson and knew he must prepare himself. He must train not only a warrior's body, but more important, a warrior's mind.

4. THE MAGIC WEAPON

With their homes and their farmland lying behind like raw, burned wounds on the face of the green earth, Blackfish and his Shawnee journeyed westward, and on the bank of the Miami River a new town, also called Piqua, became Tecumseh's new home. The little family held together loyally as the seasons changed the land, and Tecumseh grew into a youth welcomed by his foster father Blackfish on hunting forays.

The old Shawnee women clucked that there was no kinder, more generous youth than Tecumseh, for did he not share his catches with the older members of the tribe who had little? Did he not dart busily through the village when the fall winds told of winter, patching up the cabins and wigwams of those too old, too weak to find skins or wood and make the repairs for themselves? Was his voice not the first to speak out sharply when one of the young warriors bullied a boy just on the brink of manhood?

Thirteen now, lithe and strong, Tecumseh had formed definite ideas of what was right and wrong. He disliked bullying and brutality, and one day in a wrestling match with an older, stronger boy, he was surprised to find that his opponent gave up with the briefest of struggles—though his words had been the most threatening before the match began. Tecumseh observed with a quick burst of insight that perhaps often the bully's words were masks draped over his true inner fear. The truly strong man spoke quietly, for he was sure of his own will to endure.

But in his mind still raged the memory of flames and the hope of vengeance which he carried every waking moment. It was masked by a pleasant smile and a quietly forceful, though respectful, manner.

After the war between the Yankees and the Great King ended in 1781, bands of Shawnee warriors, young and fiery tempered, took to roaming south toward the Beautiful River. Many whites came along the wide, winding Ohio in their flatboats, bent on settling the rich frontier land. The Shawnee braves crept south to attack them, to stop the tide of settlement from pushing farther into the hunting lands. Against this uneasy background, in the fall of the year word passed in the Ohio country that a great tribal chieftain was journeying in their direction—Thayendanegea of the Mohawk, called Joseph Brant by the Long Knives.

Thirteen-year-old Tecumseh's mind stirred with excitement. Everyone knew the name of Brant, the Mohawk warrior whose intelligence had caught the attention years earlier of Sir William Johnson, Superintendent of Indian Affairs for the Great King in America. Johnson had personally seen to it that Brant was given a full white man's education at Moor's Indian Charity School in Lebanon, Connecticut. In this particular year, Brant was being sent westward by the Great King's government to report on the small wars flaring up beween white men and red men along the frontier.

By the light of smoldering torches Brant and seventeen Mohawk warriors, dressed only in breechcloths and beaded moccasins in spite of the cool weather, rode into Piqua. Tecumseh hovered near the council long house, snatching glimpses of Brant, hardly hoping that he would have an opportunity to speak with the great leader. But as the night darkened and Blackfish emerged with the party of Mohawks, he spied

Tecumseh in the gloom and called him to his side, presenting him to Brant.

"My adopted son." Blackfish smiled proudly. "And indeed his mind is quicker than his body, which is already the body of a warrior. One day he will be a leader among the Shawnee, or I am an exceedingly poor judge."

Brant smiled at the boy in a kindly fashion. "Walk a few steps with me, Tecumseh," he said. Tecumseh fell in beside him, his heart beating furiously with pride. "Do you find yourself filled with the ambition to become a chief?" Brant inquired.

"My desire is to kill the Long Knives who murdered my father and drove away my mother," Tecumseh replied instantly.

A frown cut Brant's forehead. "But if you are to be a leader, you must think first of your people. Thoughts of revenge are thoughts for one's self only. It is my notion that blood-thoughts can only bring more blood, and all men of our race deserve more than this."

"I . . . I do not understand," Tecumseh stammered.

They had left the others in the group a little way behind, and Brant stopped to lay his hand on the boy's shoulder. "I believe that the best road for my people, for all people of our race, is the road of reason and godliness. Rather than inflame them to fight like animals, I would inspire them to think as men. Rather than forge weapons, I would spend my time turning St. Mark's Gospel into the Mohawk tongue. Projects of this sort have occupied me for many summers, and they shall fill my mind until my spirit is taken out of my body." A warm smile relieved Brant's sober words. "Think about what I have said."

"You tell me a leader must concern himself with the good of those he leads?"

"I do, Tecumseh."

"That the way of peace is the way of a man, the way of war the way of an animal?"

"That is my feeling, my son."

"Then what are we to do when the Long Knives take our land by force?" Tecumseh replied hotly. "Sign their treaty papers?"

Brant hesitated. "The Long Knives, for the most part, are honorable men who. . ."

"Who murdered the great chief Cornstalk in a time when one of their treaties said there would be peace!" Tecumseh retorted.

Brant's head moved slowly up and down. "What you say is true. I have often thought that if the men of our race could form a mighty union—a confederation of peaceful tribes, cutting across the lines of village and single nation until we stood as one united band—we could bargain more effectively with the whites. Such a plan I should one day like to try with my own people of the Six Nations. For truly, no one tribe can claim the right to surrender land." Brant's arm lifted expansively, taking in the fragrant night darkness, the star-pointed heavens. "This land was given to all of our race, to the lowest as well as to the highest, by the Great Spirit. No one chief can sign it away at will."

"Those words I believe," Tecumseh said fervently.

Blackfish came walking up to them. "Has my adopted son been presuming upon your kindly nature by telling you tales of his prowess in the hunt, Thayendanegea?" Blackfish asked with twinkling eye.

Brant shook his head. "No. He has been speaking to me of matters of the mind. I believe that he is destined to be a leader of men as you say, for he wishes to learn the true way."

When the Mohawk party had journeyed westward again, Tecumseh could not erase the image of Brant's face from his mind, and the great chief's ideas never left his head. A leader must think of his people, not himself. The way of peace was the way of man, the way of war the way of the animal. And the thought of a powerful, single confederation of tribes, a force whose sheer strength would not require that it fight to gain its end, stirred him as no idea ever had.

Yet the mood of Brant's visit passed. "The great war is finished," Blackfish told Tecumseh wearily. "And now that the war is over, all fighting should be over also."

"It is not so, my father."

Blackfish nodded unhappily. "My people are attacked, ambushed, killed, whenever they chance to cross the trail of a Long Knife. I have heard that soon another treaty will be signed to end the fighting. Though the fighting was supposed to have stopped two years ago, this has not happened. The white men must sign still another paper to make it so. Even then, I doubt that we shall have peace. These treaties seem to me great foolishness, and not to be trusted."

"I would never sign such a paper!" Tecumseh declared hotly. "Never!"

But runners carried news into Old Piqua in 1783 that the treaty indeed had at last been signed. Scarcely a week later, two braves were shot to death in the forest across the Miami by Long Knives hunting there. A third Shawnee who escaped reported to Blackfish that the braves had fallen into a brutal ambush without a chance to fight back. Angry mutterings drifted through the village, and in the wigwam Tecumseh shared with the others of his family, he learned of a party forming to steal south to the Ohio. It was to be led by Red Foot, one of the bravest young warriors of the Shawnee.

"Red Foot goes to burn the flatboats," Tecumseh breathed excitedly. "This time I shall ask my father if I may go. If the whites who murder our people cannot be found, then other whites shall pay!" For the moment, he had completely forgotten Brant's urging of peace.

Tecumapease watched a trifle sadly as her fifteen-year-old

brother, almost as tall as a grown man now, darted from the cabin. For a moment in the firelight his face had glowed with the hatred of a man twice his years.

Blackfish listened attentively to Tecumseh's plea. At length he replied, "I am agreed, my son. You have hunted at my side during the past three years, and you have become expert with the bow and arrow. But now you are growing and it is time for you to join the attackers in a more deadly hunt. Let us find Red Foot."

In Red Foot's wigwam the hawk-faced young fighter listened with tight-clamped mouth as Tecumseh repeated his earnest request. The warrior toyed with a broad-bladed knife as the boy spoke, then raised his eyes, which glowed like coals in the smoky light.

"Do you stand beside us to kill the whites and burn their boats without mercy?" he asked quietly.

Tecumseh hesitated, his hands damp with sweat. He forced himself to say, "Yes, Red Foot, I do."

"Your knife shall take blood if you come with us."

"That . . . that is what I wish."

"Um." Red Foot grunted, hesitated a moment longer. A thin, chill smile played on his unfriendly lips. "I have heard that you can throw the spear far, Tecumseh, and that you are clever in the woods. We shall see. When the sun has risen and set twice we shall take our canoes south. Prepare yourself—and your weapons."

South through the green forests Red Foot and his war party paddled, silent ghosts on a sun-dappled river. For hours no sound could be heard but the steady bite of paddles in water. In the evening as they cooked freshly netted fish over a fire, Red Foot talked softly of the killing, the torture, the death they would bring to the whites in their boats on the Beautiful River. He spoke words which set Tecumseh aflame with the desire for vengeance, pushing thoughts of Brant completely from his mind.

There were ten of them, Tecumseh being the youngest; ten Shawnee, lying belly-down at last in the hot sun at the top of the brush-covered bluff. Below, the Beautiful River glowed hot and blue-brown in the sun, covered with a steamy haze. Tecumseh fingered his lance and peered up the silent, empty river.

Red Foot ran his bronze hand along the muzzle of the musket which he had carried from Piqua. "They will come."

A rough shake of his arm roused Tecumseh in the soft, misty light of the next dawn. Like some bony demon, Red Foot threw a finger to his lips and smiled a ghastly smile. "Roll over to the edge, little Tecumseh, and see what lies below. Then be quick and follow me. The others have already slipped down."

Lying at the crest of the bluff, Tecumseh caught his breath. Pulled up in the rushes far below lay two broad wooden flatboats. Several white men in deerskin crouched about a small fire on the bank, muskets lying near by. The aroma of cooking catfish rose upward. Along the face of the slope Tecumseh saw silent brown figures moving stealthily. His heart began to race in his chest as he dropped over the edge to follow. One of the tiny white figures kept glancing nervously out over the water. Another examined his shot pouch carefully. A third tilted a whisky jug over his arm and drank deeply.

Tecumseh crept on through the brush. The Shawnee braves had deployed into a wide semicircle, some closer to the water than others, so that a deadly ring of bows, lances, tomahawks and knives was forming silently. Tecumseh found himself at the top of the semicircle, watching the stalking from a good vantage point. Red Foot had nearly reached the water's edge, and his opposite number at the far end of the line had also.

Tecumseh counted eight Long Knives. Ten against eight. A

peculiar sensation gripped his stomach now, an urge to hurt, to wound, to kill—an emotion that came close to actual physical pain. The moving line of Shawnee, screened by thick trees and brush, halted to wait for Red Foot's signal. The sun burned hotter as it rose over the water. The minutes seemed endless. Sweat dripped from Tecumseh's back. He held the tomahawk handle, waiting. . .

To his left, one of the braves slipped and slid to one knee. A small rock went bouncing down the hillside. The white man on the bank—the one holding the jug—shrieked and pointed upward. With a guttural cry, Red Foot stood up in the bushes, musket at his shoulder, and fired. The man's jug fell with a crash as the musket ball toppled him into the water.

The braves rose and plunged down the last few yards to the clearing. Shouting with fright and excitement, the whites scrambled for their weapons. Knives glinted. A tomahawk sailed straight into the back of one of the men scrambling through the water toward his flatboat.

Tecumseh plunged on, seeing the fight, seeing the braves close in on the clearing, arms working up and down as knives cut and men cried out in agony. Then the screams stopped. Tecumseh saw Red Foot watching him, and he flung his tomahawk as he lunged through a thicket of brambles.

The two flatboats lapped softly in the water. A meadow lark rose from the brush with a flutter of wings. Red Foot thrust his lance over his head and uttered a shrill shriek of triumph.

"I wish they had lived longer," he said quietly, grinning at the eight bodies littering the bloody bank and the stained water. Then he signaled toward the boats. "Come, before we take their scalps, let us see what they carried."

Tecumseh followed his comrades into the water, clambering aboard the first of the flatboats. Suddenly the physical pain, the urge to kill, left his body as swiftly as it had come. He puzzled over his odd feelings, for he had felt a shudder of horror crawl up his spine when Red Foot said he wished the victims had lived longer. He had seen the kindly face of Joseph Brant floating in his thoughts. There had been the coldest cruelty in those words. Weakling! the boy thought unhappily to himself as he rummaged through a wooden chest in the flatboat cabin. He was not pleased with his own emotions, and to make up for this, he took Red Foot three carved powder horns and a pair of deerskin moccasins he found in the chest.

Red Foot slung the powder horns over his arm. "Did you take blood, Tecumseh?" He eyed the boy suspiciously.

"There was not time. . ." Tecumseh began.

Red Foot cut him off, hand sharply raised. "Wait! Hear!" A groan sounded again. "Yes, there! On the bank! One of the whites still breathes!" He leaped into the water and called to the others: "One still lives! See, he raises his head!"

Tecumseh followed the Shawnee to the bank. Red Foot caught the frightened white man, a stocky, yellow-haired hunter, as he tried to crawl away from the clearing. A close inspection made it clear that the man had suffered no wounds. He had apparently been struck a glancing blow on the head by a tomahawk and left for dead. The white struggled to one knee, looked around at his dead comrades, then bowed his head and closed his eyes. A terrible shuddering seized his body. As last he raised his eyes and glanced around the circle of hostile red faces, finally coming to rest on Red Foot's grim gaze.

"What . . . what air you fixin' to . . . ?" the man began in English.

Red Foot cuffed him in the face, then called:

"Bind him with thongs to that tree. Tecumseh, gather wood!"

"Wood?" Tecumseh was caught off guard. "Wood? For . . ."

Red Foot's face was ugly. "Wood to *burn him.*"

Numbly Tecumseh scurried along the bank, returning with armloads of twigs and pieces of log which he heaped at the foot of the bound white man. Red Foot, meanwhile, had been amusing himself by torturing the prisoner with the tip of his lance. The man whimpered in pain. A new sort of emotion rose to choke Tecumseh with its bitterness. At Red Foot's order one of the braves made a fire, and passed a smoldering faggot into Red Foot's hand.

"What is your name, Long Knife?" Red Foot asked in imperfect English.

"Har. . . Harper. Eli. . . Elihu Harper. For the love of God, Injun. . ."

Red Foot chuckled and passed the faggot in front of Harper's face. Several of the braves cried out in approval. The man shrieked in fright. Red Foot crouched, about to touch the faggot to the twigs and the dried grass piled over the man's moccasined feet; then he turned, looking at his men as if for a signal. The faggot smoked and sputtered in his hand. The Shawnee braves yelled approval and Red Foot's hand, moving slowly, turned the flame down toward the twigs.

Then Tecumseh was running, shouting, smashing the faggot from Red Foot's hand.

"Stop!" he cried loudly, his body trembling, his fists knotted. "Stop, stop this! *Stop this, Red Foot, it is wrong!*"

Astounded, Red Foot got to his feet.

"Little boy, you are but fifteen summers. . ." he began angrily.

"*I am old enough to know that which is evil, and that which is wrong!*" Tecumseh cried at the top of his lungs. Emotion shook him; he hardly knew what words he spoke; yet he spoke them with all the fury of a man much older. "*Are we brave men, or are we low, crouching animals of the kind that must crawl and hunt by night? I say if we burn this white man, even though he is our enemy, then may Skemotah drop us from her great net and leave us forever on earth to rot and die as cowards!"*

"I will not allow. . ." Red Foot began. But another's voice rang out.

"Quiet! Let him speak."

"He. . . he speaks with eloquence," still another muttered, eyes on the ground.

Peculiarly, Tecumseh grew calmer, for a strange thing had happened. His excited brain had paused, and he suddenly realized that words—*his* words—were working a magic, stopping bloodshed, holding back killing. He stepped forward a pace, afraid now. As Red Foot had said, he was young and had no right to speak thus to his elders. Yet he was forced to speak. . . he must speak! And though frightened, he was strangely thrilled, for the Shawnee waited, ashamed, heads turned. They waited—and Tecumseh spoke:

"To kill with honor is one thing; to butcher is another. Torturing, burning, cutting with a knife—how does it profit us? In no way! It turns us into beasts. I would be the first to step up and light the fire if I thought that it signified great courage, but suddenly I do not think it takes any courage to be cruel to a man like this, caught and helpless. No courage at all. My father died a victim of the Long Knives—murdered! But I will not let myself become the kind of animal which slew my father. I shall take vengeance on the Long Knives, but not like an animal. With courage—like a man!"

Panting, Tecumseh halted. Red Foot scowled, hesitated, then burst out:

"I say burn—"

"No!" The voice of a brave cut him off sharply. "Cut the Long Knife loose, Tecumseh. You are perhaps the wisest of us all. Your words have shown the way. Here, release him."

Tecumseh raced forward and slashed Harper's bonds. The white man staggered forward, half grinning, half crying, sputtering in English, "Thankee, boy. Thankee, Tecumsee, if that's your name. Thank—" Then very slowly he turned and walked shakily from the clearing, not looking back. Red Foot sulked, but the other members of the war party agreed with Tecumseh, and Red Foot dared not face their combined strength. The one who had spoken in Tecumseh's favor said:

"I suddenly have no more stomach for this river. Let us journey back to Piqua."

Through the forest, moving north toward home, Tecumseh grew alternately awed and triumphant as he remembered his rash action on the river's bank. He had violated all the rules of conduct for a boy his age. And yet he had found a wonderful, powerful weapon—his own thoughts, his own tongue, his own voice. Stronger than the blade, swaying men far older, turning them from cruelty and senselessness. A weapon—what a weapon! Perhaps Brant had been right after all.

On the trail back to Piqua, he vowed never to forget the weapon's strength.

5. THE PAPER OF WAYNE

As the aging Blackfish had gloomily foretold, no true peace came to the Ohio lands with the ending of the war of revolution. Colonel Ben Logan, with a company of rawboned mounted riflemen, rode up the Miami Valley to burn the Shawnee towns once more. Tecumseh's people wearily retreated to the northwest, some settling in a village called Wapakoneta, others roaming farther west into the shadowy forest lands of the state which would someday be Indiana.

Uneasily the men of the Shawnee listened to each bit of news that traveled along the frontier. The government of the mysterious and distant United States of America, Tecumseh heard, had passed what was called The Ordinance of 1787—opening a vast new empire for the whites to claim as their own. Once more Tecumseh's rage mounted. This land, the Northwest Territory, had belonged to all tribes for generations. Now the settlers rushed into it, a massive human river, ten thousand coming in a year—by flatboat, by cart, by wagon, on foot.

The Long Knives clustered together in the wilderness and raised their own towns. The following year Major General Arthur St. Clair, a soldier who had fought in the Revolution, was set up as governor of the Northwest Territory, with his headquarters at the Ohio town of Marietta. Cries of the settlers stormed in his ears: *Stop the Shawnee! Stop the Shawnee from attacking our wagons, our flatboats on the river!*

In this same year of 1788, Tecumseh, who had reached his twentieth summer, rode west of the river called Wabash, to hunt, to try to forget the great rolling white wave of settlers trampling his forest home. Time and again in the months that had passed since his fifteenth birthday, he and his older brothers had gone hunting for elk or small game in the Ohio woods, only to hear the clang of axes as settlers built cabins and villages.

Though he was growing to be a respected member in the ranks of warriors of the tribe now that he had reached young manhood, Tecumseh felt dismally that the greater power of the tribe was being chipped away. Once he had roamed freely through the forests; now he and Sauwaseekau and Cheeseekau were forced to travel prudently, watching the green trails in summer or the white trails in winter, to avoid contact with the Long Knives. While Tecumseh had lost none of his stomach for war, he felt dim inward stirrings that more important ends were in store for him—that the hour would come when the Shawnee would need leaders who thought of the people instead of themselves.

After he and Cheeseekau reached the other side of the Wabash, Tecumseh heard little of Blackfish, who had gone off to Kentucky with a war party. The days were warm and pleasant west of the Wabash where they hunted buffalo. There on the plains of Illinois, riding into buffalo herd, Tecumseh saw a massive bull break loose from the trampling horde. Wanting the bull for his own kill, he urged his pony forward. Without warning the pony's forefoot went into a hole. Tecumseh tumbled from the horse, tried to rise and fell back in pain. Cheeseekau wheeled his pony and dismounted. An examination revealed that his brother's left leg was broken.

Winter threw its first frosty cloak over the western lands.

Tecumseh had great difficulty with his broken leg, for the bones would not set properly. Time and again, thinking he was well, he rose only to find his leg buckling beneath him as new pain shot along his nerves. It was during a light snow, while Tecumseh lay uncomfortably in a bark wigwam and stared into a fire, that a messenger reported that Blackfish was dead in Kentucky.

"How did this happen?"

"There was a raid on a white settlement, O brother Tecumseh, and a white woman stabbed your father in the back with a large knife used for carving meat."

On the opposite side of the fire Cheeseekau glanced up, his dark eyes hot.

Tecumseh struggled to sit erect, wincing at the pain from his leg. "Still another debt to be paid to the whites who steal our land," he said, sadness in his voice.

At last, as the year 1789 drew to a close, Tecumseh's leg knitted and he was able to walk once more, though that leg remained forever slightly bent. News traveled swiftly now, stirring the young Shawnee's blood. The cries of the advancing settlers had finally moved St. Clair to action, and he appointed General Josiah Harmar as Commander-in-Chief of the Yankee army. Harmar gathered a force at Fort Washington on the Little Miami River to crush the wilderness people. He marched with fourteen hundred men through country settled by the Miami. Once and for all, Harmar declared to the world, the red men would understand that they did *not* own the territory above the Beautiful River.

But when the whites marched, Tecumseh was in the Ohio country again. He had offered his services to Blue Jacket, chosen the new war chief of the Shawnee, and was out recruiting braves for the coming fight. In the furious battle which marked the beginning of new warfare on the frontier, Harmar was bitterly defeated. As the Long Knives fell back, Blue Jacket and Little

Turtle, the wily leader of the Miami, rejoiced. But only for a short time.

General St. Clair himself led the next attack in the following year. Already known to Blue Jacket and Little Turtle for his bravery and cleverness, Tecumseh found himself a vital part of the campaign. On November 4, 1791, St. Clair's army of two thousand was crushed and turned back by Little Turtle of the Miami, Blue Jacket of the Shawnee and Buckongahelos of the Delaware. Throughout the battle Tecumseh scouted, skillfully leading small bands of braves to attack the flanks of the embattled whites. As the St. Clair army dragged itself homeward toward Marietta, a sad cavalcade of bloodied, tattered soldiers, Tecumseh was pleased that the whites had been decisively turned back. They had learned that they could not claim the red men's land by force.

Then word came from Cheeseekau to the south. The Cherokee were rising and Tecumseh journeyed to fight at his brother's side. One black night, seven hundred red men—mostly Cherokee, but including many braves from other tribes—launched a fierce, howling attack on Buchanan's Station. Musket fire tore the night for several hours as the battle raged back and forth. Finally Cheeseekau seized his brother's arm.

"Make me a torch," he demanded. "I must climb the blockhouse and fire the roof."

Reluctantly Tecumseh fashioned the torch for his older brother. Sporadic shots rattled in the clearing around the stockade as a shadowy figure inched up the roughhewn blockhouse wall bearing the unlit firebrand. If Cheeseekau could reach the roof and ignite the torch and leave it there to burn, Buchanan's Station might yet fall to the Cherokee.

A shot crashed in the darkness. Cheeseekau pitched away from the blockhouse into the air. A cheer went up from some hidden white marksmen. When Tecumseh reached his brother's side, Cheeseekau was dead. Tecumseh bent his head, fighting back the tears that welled in his eyes.

The Cherokee uprising failed. But already new danger threatened, north of the Ohio. Another army, mightier than those of Harmar and St. Clair, was being gathered for a new attack. A runner came to summon Tecumseh, for Blue Jacket wanted his young aide at his side in the forthcoming clash. Tecumseh was now a hard, seasoned warrior of twenty-four. He stood a little under six feet, with thick black hair, heavy eyebrows, startling white teeth and hazel eyes. As he rode to join Blue Jacket he had the feeling that destiny had something in store for him. What this destiny might be he could not yet say, but it waited there where the Blacksnake coiled.

The general was called Mad Anthony Wayne, or the General Who Never Sleeps, or the Blacksnake—this last a tribute to his slow but deadly movement in the field. At an angry council meeting Tecumseh had heard Little Turtle urge peace with this feared Long Knife warrior. Blue Jacket had smitten Little Turtle across the face, calling him a coward. In an instant, Little Turtle's power as a leader was finished and Blue Jacket had taken command. He had appointed Tecumseh his chief spy, to watch the movement of the Blacksnake near his lair at Cincinnati along the Ohio.

Wayne marched on October 7, 1793, with three thousand, six hundred regular soldiers. As he moved north he built forts—Hamilton, St. Clair, Greenville, Recovery, Defiance. He spent the winter at Greenville, while in the white-blanketed forest Tecumseh and his small band of spies watched and waited. Then in the summer of 1794 the Blacksnake uncoiled and stretched out to strike.

Blue Jacket, hopelessly outnumbered, assembled fourteen hundred men. Wayne moved down the left bank of the Maumee, his men riding blooded Kentucky horses, his artillery ready, his foot soldiers fixing bayonets on their muskets. On August 20th, where a fearsome tornado had once blown great trees to the ground, the Battle of Fallen Timbers was fought.

The battle opened with a desperate attack by Tecumseh's scouts against the head of Wayne's column, which was advancing toward the jumble of great tree trunks. Gunfire crashed in the forest as Wayne's soldiers began to spread out. Tecumseh's scout group was driven back into a dense thicket, where one of the fallen trees made a natural protective barrier.

Bullets buzzed and snapped through the thicket. Suddenly Sauwaseekau came running up. "Listen!" he called. "A sound of hoofs."

Tecumseh scowled. "Wayne brings his horse soldiers. It will go badly for. . ."

A sudden shot crashed in the thicket. Sauwaseekau cried out and pitched over. Stunned by the horror of what had happened, Tecumseh moved clumsily, trying to find time for thought. Hoofbeats thundered in the forest. Down the line shrill cries of fright told that the Indian line was breaking. Tecumseh turned to see his scouts rushing from the thicket.

"There are wounded!" he called after them.

"But the horse soldiers come! We cannot stop them!" they answered.

"There are wounded to be carried back," Tecumseh insisted. He rallied a small knot of warriors and forced them by sheer strength of will to carry their injured comrades back along the line of retreat. In a small glade he came across a dead horse and one of Wayne's troops, his uniform daubed with blood. The soldier, biting his lips and awaiting the death blow, raised a hand protectively when he saw Tecumseh.

Tecumseh shook his head and ran on past the glade, leaving the astounded white soldier to be rescued by the advancing lines of Wayne's force. As he ran, Tecumseh thought grimly, *what is one life spared if a tiny drop of the blood of the animal is replaced by a drop of the blood of the reasonable man?*

But the defeat was a bitter one, for the army of red warriors broke, scattered and ran.

Triumphantly Wayne burned the Indian villages. The red man's strength was shattered in the Ohio country; Tecumseh realized this unhappily as he retreated to Buck Creek with a few good friends he had gathered during the campaigns of the last few years. Deep in the forest Tecumseh heard news that the Blacksnake had built Fort Wayne in September and then returned to Greenville to stay the winter. With him had gone a man Tecumseh had glimpsed in the fighting at Fallen Timbers —a man whose name he had heard only once: Lieutenant William Henry Harrison, Wayne's aide. Tecumseh dismissed the young officer from his mind, never believing he would see him again.

Along the shores of Buck Creek Tecumseh camped with perhaps fifty friends, young warriors of the Shawnee, the Miami and the Delaware. They ranged through the forest, crying shrilly in their mock battles, for Tecumseh found that leading his friends in practice warfare helped put down the bitterness of defeat that still lingered after Fallen Timbers. Though invited to attend the treaty-making following the battle, he had refused, preferring the solitude of the forest.

The days passed pleasantly enough for a time. The braves hunted, chipped arrows from flint and talked much of the state of the red man in the Ohio country.

"It is my belief," Tecumseh said one evening, as they were gathered around the campfire, "that a line must be drawn and never passed—a line to separate forever our lands from those of the Long Knives." He raised his head in the firelight. "Long ago the great gods who built the world drew that line for us."

"A treaty line?" asked Winged Fox, a Miami.

Tecumseh's finger traced a curve in the dust. "The Ohio—the Beautiful River. North of that, we rule. South of that, the whites must stay."

Running Arrow, a thin-cheeked young man of the Delaware tribe, snorted. "Already they have crossed the line a thousand times, and then again a thousand."

"They would not have crossed," Tecumseh replied softly, "had I been leader."

Winged Fox leaned forward, his black eyes brilliant in the glow of the fire. "Already there are many in the tribes—young men, not old and withered sachems—who whisper that you could have led a victory at the field of fallen trees."

"Perhaps," Tecumseh mused. "That is foolish speculation in any case."

"While the old chiefs tremble and sign lands away," Running Arrow added quickly, "many warriors call you chief."

Tecumseh shook his head. "No, I am not the tribal war chief. Nor even a chief of a village."

"We call you a chief greater than these," Winged Fox said fervently, rising to his feet. "The chief of the Beautiful River. The chief of the Ohio—the leader of *all* the tribes. If you would only lead, many would follow."

Around the campfire other voices called assent. Tecumseh gazed from one face to the next, warily, afraid it might be a dream, a delusion born of his strange feelings of his own destiny. Did they truly speak of him as a chief greater than the tribal war sachems? Greater than the powerful rulers of the Indian towns? Tecumseh's mind stirred with excitement.

In the autumn of 1795 Blue Jacket and a small band of braves rode across Buck Creek, and the old and once-mighty war chief sat beside Tecumseh again, his face lined and worn. Tecumseh welcomed him politely, yet sat a bit haughtily, aloof, as the two feasted beside the fire while the fall wind cried eerily outside.

"I have come, Tecumseh," Blue Jacket began uncertainly, "to explain to you the treaty which I signed in the spring at Greenville."

"This treaty of Greenville I have heard about."

"Did not the Blacksnake say you would be welcome there, as the others of the tribes were welcomed?" Blue Jacket asked.

"I was asked to go to the peace meeting, yes. I did not go because long ago I learned that words on paper have small meaning; especially words put there by the Long Knives. Were many at Greenville?"

Blue Jacket nodded. He seemed listless, defeated, his face empty of courage. "More than a thousand. Ninety-two sachems, of which. . ."

Tecumseh's eyes shone hard in the firelight.

"What tribes?"

"Eh?"

"What tribes signed away the land of our fathers which they do not own?"

Blue Jacket hesitated, then spoke: "Wyandot, Shawnee. . ."

"*I* am Shawnee. *I* was not there."

Blue Jacket squinted into the fire, unwilling to start an argument. "The Delaware also, and the Ottawa, Chippewa, Potawatomi, Kickapoo, Kaskaskia, Wea, Piankashaw, the Eel River tribes. . ."

Tecumseh spat into the fire with contempt.

"You signed this paper?"

"I did, because I believed it best. I believed it would bring peace."

Tecumseh raised one hand sharply. "I will hear no more."

"I have come to plead that you accept the treaty for the good of all your brethren."

"It is not for my good or yours, or any of the tribes!" Tecumseh raged in soft fury. "You cannot see the truth behind this paper? It is worthless, like all the papers of the Long Knives. They will continue to whittle our land away to nothing, bringing whites by the thousands. I will refuse to honor the paper. And there are others who feel the same way." He hesitated. "They came to me, unhappy, from Greenville. They heard me say that I did not believe in such paper-signing. They are my brothers and will do as I say."

Blue Jacket said wearily, "We were well treated by Wayne. Let me speak to you about his fairness."

Tecumseh sat in stony silence for a moment, then reluctantly agreed. "Because you are my friend and have been my great leader I shall listen."

Wayne had called the treaty council in the spring. The tribes had arrived at Greenville and immediately inquired when the money would be distributed. Wayne answered, "Tomorrow." Always tomorrow! From June 16th until August 10th the sachems sat with Wayne in council, and each day it was, "Tomorrow." At last the treaty agreements were drawn up, establishing what the whites called the Greenville Treaty Line. It ran roughly across the middle of the Ohio country, east to west from the Cuyahoga River to Fort Recovery, and thence south to the Beautiful River. All lands south and east of the line were given by the red men to the whites, twenty-five thousand square miles in exchange for twenty thousand dollars in trade goods and a promise of future cash payments of roughly ten thousand dollars. When the crude marks of the sachems were on the paper, Wayne gave a signal and tomahawks were sunk into the whisky casks. Liquor flowed. Sachems and warriors drank and ate—and half of the Ohio hunting lands were gone.

"The talk of firewater reminds me," Blue Jacket spoke absently. "Your brother sat at Greenville also."

"Laulewasika?"

"Even so. He cried eagerly after the firewater, and I am

sorry to tell his brother that he is even now a man who drinks to excess. He was seldom conscious, seldom able to speak with a straight tongue, though he is still a young man."

Tecumseh nodded. "He was always a strange child. I have heard many reports of his drunkenness. I have not seen him for a long time." His mind drifted hazily for a moment to the happy family of his youth. Cheeseekau and Sauwaseekau were dead, slain by the Long Knives. His younger brother and sister he had not seen in a year. Word passed that they had journeyed west to the Missouri lands with a group of Shawnee similar to the one that had led his mother away. Shawnee frightened of battle, seeking refuge from danger. The littlest brother was a hopeless drunkard. But Tecumapease and Nehaaeemo had made good lives for themselves, the former marrying Wasegoboah, a strong young Shawnee brave, and the latter becoming the bride of George Ironsides, a Scottish trader in the Maumee Valley, who was reported to be a kindly man in spite of his white skin.

The thoughts brought a final note of unhappiness to Tecumseh as he sat with Blue Jacket. His shoulders sloped for a moment and he stared moodily into the fire.

"Consider again, my brother," Blue Jacket said. "You could do much to help our cause by speaking out that the treaty-signing was good. There are many who listen to you for guidance."

"Words are wasted, Blue Jacket. You have signed the paper and cannot violate it because your word, like mine, is to be trusted. Yet by signing, you have agreed that what the Blacksnake and his people did is right—you have said, yes, you are right to take away the lands which belong to us. You have said that the lands do not belong to us at all, and that an army—any army—can force us to give away these lands which are the birthright of all the tribes. This lesson I learned well from the great Mohawk Brant: The land belongs to every man. I will not sign, nor will I say the signing was right."

Eventually Blue Jacket rose. "The wind is cold tonight. I shall return to my wigwam."

"In the morning perhaps we could hunt the elk," Tecumseh said.

"No." Blue Jacket smiled wanly. "We are friends, but we can no longer be brothers. Perhaps you are wise. Perhaps I have been foolish. I do not wish to look on your face for fear I see my own shame."

Tecumseh touched Blue Jacket's old bronzed arm. "My own sorrow is deep that I have caused my friend pain. But I. . . I must go my way alone. You are Blue Jacket. I. . ."

Their eyes met. Tecumseh's body had straightened, strong now, even haughty, for he sensed his power fully, the power he could use, *must* use, if he was to protect his people—those who could not protect themselves from the papers of Wayne. This sense of importance frightened him as he finished his sentence:

"I. . . I am Tecumseh, whom some call the chief of the Ohio."

Blue Jacket stumbled off wearily into the dusk, nodding, for he had heard the name before. And when the spring of 1796 came, Tecumseh and a band of those who listened to his voice rode west toward a new home on the Whitewater River in the Indiana land—a home beyond the treaty line.

6.

REBECCA

Toward the close of an April twilight a single rider on a pony stood outlined against the soft orange sky on a hill not far from where the village of Old Chillicothe had once stood. Below the rise, beyond a planted field, a small farmhouse nestled in the dusk, its windows yellow with friendly lamplight. A curl of wood smoke ghosted up the chimney toward the patches of bright sky in the west. For several minutes the thirty-year-old Tecumseh gazed down at the house, wanting to ride toward the welcoming light, yet oddly afraid, filled with emotions he did not quite understand.

At last he urged the pony forward with a gentle pressure of his knees.

The frontier had quieted briefly during the past two years, and the camp on the Whitewater had grown to a thriving village of four hundred, with Tecumseh as the acknowledged chief. There, in the land of the Miami, the Potawatomi and the Illinois, Tecumseh had broadened his influence, hunting with the sachems of the various villages, preaching quietly but with little success his doctrine that the land belonged to all men and that white advances should be resisted. Though personally admired for his strength, his intelligence and his hunting prowess, Tecumseh failed to stir his new-found friends to action. In truth, little action was required, since the land of the red men in the country of his adopted home had not yet suffered as greatly from the encroachments of the Long Knives.

So Tecumseh supervised his little village, overseeing a rich corn crop, making sure those who looked to him for leadership were amply provided for. The only event marring the relative peace of the two years was an unhappy marriage to Manete, a half-breed Shawnee woman considerably older than Tecumseh. The marriage ended when he cast her out of his wigwam, thoroughly sickened by her crude ways, her lack of understanding of his ideas and her generally shiftless nature. The marriage had been a dreadful mistake, he realized, and he had taken the step only because tribal tradition and the pressures of those around him dictated some degree of conformity to ancient ritual.

Thus, in 1798 he grew weary of the Whitewater village and turned his pony back toward the old hunting grounds in Ohio, to see again the land of his childhood, to shut out the grim memories of a bad marriage and to visit with his sisters and their husbands.

The visits over, he found himself outside the farmhouse at twilight. He dismounted at the edge of the field and walked through the shadows to the house. He knocked softly and in a moment the door opened. A white man in homespun clothing leaned forward to peer more closely at his visitor. Then his face relaxed good-humoredly and he spoke in Shawnee:

"Welcome, Tecumseh! Welcome to my house. Come in."

"Thank you, Galloway," Tecumseh replied, stepping forward.

Though he treated the settler James Galloway with formal courtesy, he did not fear him. They had met during the winter at a near-by trading station during Tecumseh's visit with Nehaaeemo and her husband Ironsides. Tecumseh had at first been suspicious of Galloway's offer of friendship and exchange of hunting information. Then he had grown fascinated as Galloway talked of the books he owned—more than three hundred of them, carefully carried across mountains and down the Ohio to Galloway's new home in Greene County. The books were Galloway's most valued possession. And though he was no stranger to the savage trails crisscrossing the wilderness—he had hunted with George Rogers Clark—he was a scholarly, thoughtful man. Tecumseh's glimpse of the worlds of knowledge which lay in Galloway's books had aroused the Shawnee's eager mind.

Tecumseh stood rather shyly as the white man introduced him, using English, to his wife and four sons.

Answering awkwardly and briefly in his own language to each introduction, Tecumseh caught his breath when Galloway presented the final member of his family. Turning from an iron kettle bubbling on the hearth, the young girl, named Rebecca, smiled at Tecumseh. This very nearly sent him fleeing from the house. She put terror in his heart, for never had he seen any young woman, white or Shawnee, so lovely as this yellow-haired daughter of the settler. She seemed as gentle as his wife Manete had been coarse. Her clear blue eyes met his gaze for a moment. Then she turned away, primly, as was proper for unmarried women. Galloway smiled. His small sons gaped openmouthed at the tall, tanned Shawnee. At last Tecumseh managed to speak to Galloway:

"Since you told me of the books, I have been eager to return here to hunt, but have had no chance until now. Have I upset your household?"

James Galloway chuckled. "Not a bit. Would you eat with us?"

"I cooked a bit of dried buffalo at sundown. I. . . I would look on the books, if I may."

"Right through here," the white man began, starting for a curtained doorway. He paused. "No, on second thought. . . Becky, will you show our guest the library?" To the Shawnee he added, "My children have all been taught the tongues of the tribes, you see. Out here English is the new language, and there are few of us speaking it, compared to so many using your tongue."

"More who speak your tongue come each day," Tecumseh said.

Galloway nodded a bit uneasily. The young Rebecca moved softly forward with a rustle of skirts and directed Tecumseh through the doorway. She lit a lamp on a table and shyly indicated the homemade shelving which housed the row of books. The lamp's glow flickered on elaborate bindings. Tecumseh ran his hand almost reverently across the spines of the books. He drew one halfway from a shelf, then, embarrassed, swung to face the girl. "May I touch it, or is this forbidden?"

"Of course not," Rebecca laughed softly. "Take any one you choose, Tecumseh." Her Shawnee, while it was spoken slowly and with much thought, was good. "Books are not meant to sit on a shelf and gather dust and be admired only for their fine covers. You should read and learn from them."

"In all these books there must be much that would benefit a man." Tecumseh drew a thick, heavy volume from its place. Again he felt an emotion very close to fear. The powerful spell of the books reminded him somehow of the great powers which ruled the earth, of spirits rushing through the air to final resting places, of all things magical and mysterious. He opened the book and peered at the small, closely set lines of type which held no meaning for him. On one page he paused to gaze at a crude illustration of a man holding aloft a bare human skull, staring at it sadly. Rebecca stepped close to examine the drawing.

"That is—" She labored to speak the English word for him. "Ham-let."

"Ham-let?" The syllables rolled awkwardly on his tongue.

"Yes. He was a prince of his people in a country very far

away. But he was not a real person, you see. He was just a. . . well, a character in a story that is not real. This book has many stories in it, all written by the same man. His name was Shakespeare."

"Why read Shakes-peare if he does not write of true things?" Tecumseh puzzled.

"Because many of the things he wrote *about* people are true, although none of the *people* are real and. . . Oh, can you understand me? I speak so badly."

"I understand. The man who wrote this book was a wise man, you say."

"That's right. And the words—his language—it has a beautiful sound. To know that, though, one must read English."

"I cannot read it or speak it. But I wish I might, so that I could gather all the wisdom of these books into my head, and be a better man because of it."

For a few moments longer in the lamplight Rebecca hesitated. Then, swept up by the strange, swift understanding which had arisen between them, she blurted, "I would teach you English, Tecumseh, if only you would come often to my father's house."

"This land is no longer my home. I come here only to hunt and visit my sisters. This time I came to see the books. My home lies that way, where the sun falls beneath the edge of the earth at night. But I will stay in the Ohio country a time, if your father will allow me in his house to sit at your feet and learn. I will come often to read the books and speak the tongue which will help me."

Rebecca clasped her hands delightedly, then turned away with a blush. Tecumseh inquired what was wrong. He received no answer and grew alarmed. The situation was saved by the appearance of James Galloway in the door.

"Tecumseh, my wife's cooking a special dish in your honor.

Will you come have a portion with us? My sons can hardly sit still, knowing there is a Shawnee sachem in the house."

"A sachem?" Rebecca asked, startled.

Galloway nodded. "Yes, daughter. The name Tecumseh is a mighty one on the frontier these days. Our guest is a very powerful and influential young man. He is the only important warrior who refused to sign Wayne's treaty. There are many who say he was right."

"Let me not be the warrior, my friend, but the pupil, when I visit your house."

"Fair enough," Galloway grinned. "Come on now, before—" He switched to English and finished "—before those young'uns of mine bust a seam giggling out there by the fire."

Tecumseh followed father and daughter to the hearthside. A new, exciting sense of strength filled him as he dined and carried on polite conversation with the family. His eyes strayed restlessly again and again, first to the curtained door behind which rested the books, then to the face of the young Rebecca. Not one treasure had he found here in the house of this warm-hearted white man, but two.

And so it was that as the year 1798 grew older, Tecumseh lingered, hunting in Ohio, returning often to the farm of James Galloway. He and Rebecca located a shady spot near an arbor where the lessons began. Rebecca was a kind, patient teacher. She guided his study of English carefully, taught him new words every day. Shortly after sunup each morning he would return from the place where he slept on the ground near the arbor, and Rebecca would begin their lesson, using the family Bible as her first text. Summer passed too quickly. The lessons moved indoors again.

By this time Tecumseh could understand the words she read to him, and he could also read quite a few of them himself. A special favorite of his was the play in which he had seen the picture of the young man with the skull. Prince Hamlet appealed to him because the prince of Denmark, too, was dedicated to paying back his father's murderers. Then, in the history of the wondrous empire of Alexander the Great, Tecumseh found another model on which to pattern his hopes and his gathering dreams.

Strongly religious, Rebecca also read frequently from the New Testament. She encouraged Tecumseh's faith in God, and in the humble carpenter who had died on a wooden cross to save his people—all people. He was a man who had believed in treating the poor and the helpless with compassion, as Tecumseh did.

"Turn again to the story of Moses, please, Rebecca," Tecumseh would say most often. His eyes, empty of harshness now, were filled with some strange, magnificent dream. Rebecca read softly by the firelight as her father snored gently near by:

"*. . . and Moses stretched out his hand over the sea, and the Lord caused the sea to go back by a strong east wind all that night, and made the sea dry land, and the waters were divided. And the children of Israel went into the midst of the sea upon the dry ground, and the waters were a wall unto them on their right hand, and on their left . . .*"

"If I could only be such a great leader of my people," Tecumseh murmured softly.

Rebecca paused, her eyes warm and gentle. "I think someday you will be a great man, Tecumseh. I have felt it from the very start. I. . . I don't know why. . . but. . ." Again embarrassed, she bent her head over the book and read:

"*. . . and the waters returned and covered the chariots, and the horsemen, and all the host of Pharaoh that came into the sea after them; there remained not so much as one of them.*"

In a moment, when Rebecca had finished this fourteenth chapter of Exodus, Tecumseh found himself gazing at her, his brain in a turmoil.

"Is. . . is something wrong?" Rebecca asked.

"Read again," Tecumseh muttered, confused and upset.

Rebecca shook her head and replied, "No, you must read now." She handed him the massive Bible. Tecumseh felt her fingers brush the back of his hand for a moment. He closed his eyes and prayed fervently for help.

His brain reeled with fright. He knew at last, knew with certainty, what he had felt the past months—that he loved this girl Rebecca Galloway and that he would never love any other woman. Knowing this frightened the warrior who had fought the mightiest of the Yankee armies in the bloody battle for the Ohio country. He must leave, and quickly, to settle his thoughts.

Before dawn he arose, and using a flimsy excuse rode from the farm leaving a mystified Galloway to wonder at the sudden, peculiar behavior of the Shawnee brave just passing out of sight beyond the west pasture.

Winter wrapped its whiteness about the Galloway farm. Through the snow-covered field Tecumseh came riding slowly one morning. James Galloway, attending to his livestock in his crude wooden barn, noticed the Shawnee approaching and hurried outside to greet him. The bags of animal skins hanging across the back of his pony bulged heavily. Galloway took a closer look at the birchbark canoe dragged, travois fashion, behind the animal. Tecumseh dismounted. His face had thinned somewhat and was set in serious lines. He looked to Galloway as though some heavy problem had occupied his mind since last he visited the farm.

"It is good to see my Shawnee brother," Galloway said.

"In my pouches are gifts," Tecumseh replied. "Large silver

hair combs traded from the whites, and beaver pelts which I have trapped myself. This canoe also is a gift for your daughter Rebecca. I come with these gifts to ask whether I may take her as my wife."

"Your. . ." Galloway gasped. His brows pulled together thoughtfully for a moment. "As far as what I have to say about the matter. . ."

Impulsively Tecumseh grasped Galloway's arm. "I will give fifty silver brooches for her!"

". . . what *I* say, Tecumseh, doesn't make much difference." He smiled. "You had better ask Rebecca yourself. She must make up her own mind. She's inside the house."

Resolutely Tecumseh walked toward the farm kitchen. His swift, proud stride never once betrayed the trembling uncertainty he felt in his heart. Rebecca had no chance to speak before Tecumseh drew himself to his full height. In a commanding voice which again hid his fear of rejection, he proclaimed:

"Rebecca Galloway, I come to ask you to be my wife."

And then, in a rush of words, he poured out to her the story of the unhappy time he had spent as the husband of the woman Manete, who was not kind enough or good enough to inspire in him the sort of love he felt for Rebecca.

Slowly, while the fire crackled on the kitchen hearth, the girl stretched out her hand and touched his arm. Her eyes softened as she looked into his eyes.

"Yes, Tecumseh," Rebecca said, "I will marry you. My love for you is as deep as your love is for me. But there are two things I must ask of you, if we are to be happy together."

"Name them," the Shawnee said, his heart bursting with joy.

"First," Rebecca said, "I would like to be married by a minister of God, in a Christian ceremony."

"Gladly," Tecumseh said. "You know how I feel about your wonderful Bible."

"And second—" The girl paused, then gathered strength and went on. "Second, you must give up your life as an Indian and live as a white man."

Tecumseh was shocked numb. This was a condition he had not expected.

"I love you very much, Rebecca," he said haltingly. "But I cannot answer you now. I must be alone and settle my mind." Without another word he went out of the kitchen again, mounted his pony and rode out toward the white-blanketed hills. A month passed—a month Tecumseh spent in the cold, wind-whipped winter wilderness, struggling with his doubts, his fears and the love he felt for Rebecca. At last he returned to the small farm.

On a black December night torn by the first white traces of a coming blizzard, James Galloway summoned his daughter outside the farmhouse, then vanished back inside. Rebecca lifted a lantern, and in the dim light she thought she detected tears in the warrior's eyes. But only for an instant.

"I have searched what is in my heart," Tecumseh said slowly and with obvious pain. "But though I love you deeply, I cannot renounce my people."

"If you do love me. . ." Rebecca began unhappily.

"I love my people also, Rebecca. They have desperate need of me. You are white. Your life can be a happy one. But my people are pushed, hounded, hunted like animals, driven from the very land on which they were born. Not the Shawee alone, but all of the tribes suffer. There will come a time, I think, when they shall need me very much, and I must be ready. I am not so foolish as to consider myself a holy man as was the great leader Moses, but I shall follow his example."

The lantern crashed into the snow, flickering feebly. Rebecca covered her face with hands already blue from the night cold.

"You have taught me much of kindness and goodness and wisdom," Tecumseh said slowly. Each new word brought fresh torment, yet he had to go on. "No other woman's face shall ever seem as fair as yours, and no other woman shall I ever call my wife. I will love you until the moment of my death, Rebecca, even though we may never meet again."

Blinded by his own unhappiness, he struggled to speak more and could not. Quickly he turned and ran into the darkness. The hoofs of a pony thudded briefly. The wind shrieked. The lantern snuffed out at last, and in the stormy darkness Rebecca wept for the man she would never see again.

Tecumseh looked back, but the lights of James Galloway's farmhouse had vanished behind the seething fury of the blizzard.

7. THE COMING OF THE PROPHET

Two dollars! Two dollars an acre, that's all, two dollars . . . !

In the swarming cities of the east coast of the new American nation in that year of 1799, the cries of the land speculators stopped many a man, set many a head looking toward the sunset, started many a wheel turning over the Alleghenies to the rich, raw, green country of the frontier. There a man who had worked for someone else could now stand alone, owner of his own little kingdom—his own farm—at two dollars an acre, yessiree, *two dollars. . .* It was the lure of owning the earth that drew them, these upstart Yankees who had defeated the mighty British Empire less than twenty years earlier; these poor families with their few goods and their rickety wagons who once, in Europe, where they or their parents had lived, could never have dreamed of owning land, let alone at the tiny price of only *Yessir, you heard me correctly, Sir. I said two dollars per acre for the finest farmland on the continent. It's all part of the United States now, it belongs to those who take it. . .*

Far west of the teeming cities, and all the smaller New Yorks and Baltimores and Philadelphias which daily poured forth their stream of immigrants, Tecumseh roamed and hunted restlessly, shedding day by day a bit of the terrible grief which had fallen upon his heart when he left Rebecca.

Sadly he saw the timber hacked, the land cleared, the tide of wagons and flatboats pushing constantly forward, driving his people back, farther back, farther west.

In 1800, with the Ohio Territory eligible for statehood, the Indiana Territory was organized. Forest runners carried news the following year that the power of the Long Knives was coming to rule the territory along the Wabash. William Henry Harrison resigned from the House of Representatives in which he had served as delegate from the Indiana Territory, and set forth from Vincennes on the Wabash River.

"Governor?" Tecumseh spoke, frowning at the messenger.

"Yes, O Chief, the arm of the Long Knives, strong with many soldiers."

Tecumseh scowled at a dancing fire in the twilight glade.

"They took our lands above the Beautiful River, and now they try to seize the Wabash lands as well. No!" Raging, furious, he smacked a fist against his thigh. "I do not like it that Harrison is their sachem. He fought with the Blacksnake at the field of the Fallen Timbers, and he is not a friend."

"Then the need for you among our people is greater than ever," said the other.

Tecumseh gave no reply. He stared into the sputtering flames, Rebecca's name whispering in his mind. The truth of the messenger's words was like a bitter medicine. Yet in the cool of night, with the red fox's eye gleaming cruelly through a clump of brush and a white moon sailing above the timber, such power, such respect, seemed of little value. Rebecca . . .!

But always at the end of his sad pattern of thought came the memory that he, not Rebecca, had made the decision. He had chosen the way of his people over the way of happiness.

Tecumseh rode back and forth from the Greenville Line to the Wabash during the next few years, living a while with this tribe, hunting a while with that. He was welcomed because of the shrewdness of his mind, and the older men frequently called upon him to settle disputes. His popularity grew and when he spoke, eloquently, fluently, others listened. As the years passed, as he became older than thirty summers, the weapon of speech discovered along the Ohio became his most powerful ally.

If the hand of one brave was raised falsely and treacherously against another, Tecumseh spoke, and the accuser—favorite of all the tribe, while the accused was but an outcast—suffered just punishment.

If a powerful warrior stole from a weaker one, Tecumseh meted out the proper penalty for coveting the goods of another.

If the sachems talked of a battle between tribes—a battle to decide who should recognize a certain creek as boundary of their hunting lands—Tecumseh spoke, and each tribe roamed freely on either side of the little watercourse. When he spoke, they saw that the land belonged to all.

But out of the east was coming the firewater. And during those first five years of the nineteenth century, the journeying Tecumseh observed its ghastly effects upon his people. Drunkenness was a plague, turning men of the tribes away from their families, their hunting, their own true way of life. Tecumseh never drank. He had tasted the white man's whisky but once, and felt its soddening, mind-shaking effect. The firewater weakened his people, and if they were ever to make a final stand against the whites, they must not be weak, but strong.

To increase Tecumseh's sorrow even further, it was widely known along the Indiana frontier that one of the worst drunkards among all the red nations was the shiftless and immoral Laulewasika. Tecumseh had seen his younger brother only a few times since their childhood, and there had never been any great affection between them. Yet the tales of the one-eyed Laulewasika's debauchery made his heart all the more heavy.

See what the firewater does! Tecumseh would think to himself. Is Laulewasika so foolish that he cannot know that one of his eyes is sightless because of his very drunkenness? He had put out his own eye when an arrow split in two—an arrow he had been trying to send aloft in the midst of a drunken stupor.

Then a strange miracle was told to him in 1805, a few miles above Vincennes along the Wabash.

Tecumseh was preparing to set out for a leisurely hunt one morning when a hail went up from the sun-dappled water. Around a brush-clustered bank nosed a canoe. Tecumseh leaped to his feet, knife drawn and instantly ready. Then a smile crossed his face. He recognized Wolf In The Hill, his occasional hunting companion, a member of the Wea tribe. Tecumseh hailed the younger man and they had breakfast together, renewing their friendship.

At last Wolf In The Hill said, "Wondrous things have happened to Laulewasika, the brother of Tecumseh."

The Shawnee smiled bitterly. "He perhaps drinks wondrous quantities of the evil whisky, that's all."

Wolf In The Hill shook his head decisively. "Laulewasika no longer drinks."

"It sounds as if it is *you* who have fuddled your head with the firewater, Wolf In The Hill."

"I do not lie! I have come from the White River, where Laulewasika has gathered people around him to preach his new beliefs."

"What sort of beliefs?"

"Holy ones, Tecumseh. Laulewasika has become a holy man. He fears the Almighty Spirit."

"I cannot believe it."

"There were white holy men in his camp also," Wolf In The Hill said.

"White men?" Tecumseh exclaimed. "Which ones?"

"Have you not heard of the Shakers?"

"Those strange holy men who leap and twist themselves and shake their bodies and thus come close to the Spirit, according to their way of thinking? Yes, I know of the Shakers. They are among the few good white men who have reached this land."

"Laulewasika was with the Shakers on the White River. With my own ears I heard him preach to the people there. He implored them to refrain from the whisky."

Tecumseh scrambled to his feet. Deep in his mind he yearned to believe. If the story were true it would be a wonderful thing for Laulewasika, for himself, for all the Indian people. "Wolf In The Hill," he said swiftly, "I shall go to my brother to see this mystical change which has come about. I thank you for telling me."

The Shawnee then gathered his few belongings, nosed his canoe into the Wabash and disappeared from sight.

Indeed Wolf In The Hill had not lied. Tecumseh and Laulewasika greeted one another shyly, the latter wearing a tattered scrap of cloth to conceal his ruined eye. Then the two men retired to the younger brother's crude wigwam, so that they could talk in private.

"The word reached me that you no longer poison yourself with the white man's whisky," Tecumseh said.

"That is true." Laulewasika's good eye had a piercing, hypnotic quality. "Only a few months before, in the spring, I grew suddenly sickened of my sinning. I shrieked aloud for the Great Spirit to show me a way of escape from the hell which my sotted body had become. I was in a very lonely clearing. It was dawn. A strange whitish mist coiled on the ground, and I thought death was upon me."

He leaned forward, his voice softening. Unaccountably Tecumseh found himself fascinated by the sincerity of his brother's words. Laulewasika *had* become a different man.

"My brain went dark and I fell into a strange sleep, with

the cold mist creeping around my throat. I suddenly saw a forest path, and I stood at a place where the path led both right and left. To the right lay peace, forgiveness. To the left—torment. In my peculiar dream I became very cold, knowing that the Great Spirit had given me a choice. Yet I chose the left branch, for that was my life—the road of evil traveled by those who have seen their own evil and cannot escape it. Upon this path I saw three cabins. At the first cabin there was a second path which led back to the right-hand road. At the second cabin also a road. At the third cabin—"

He raised his one burning eye.

"None. No path. For that last house was death."

Tecumseh, in spite of himself, blurted, "Did the dream end there, Laulewasika?"

"No. I turned and ran back to the second cabin, and crossed to the true way where there was peace, where houses glowed with the holy light of the Great Spirit. And I awakened in the clearing knowing I had become a new man."

A brief grunt escaped Tecumseh's lips. Was his brother mad? Possibly. His voice had a singsong pitch. Yet Tecumseh did not doubt that Laulewasika's change of heart was all for the better.

"As I rode into your village I saw many people."

"Perhaps a hundred," Laulewasika nodded. "They follow me—and I teach them of what I learned in the dream."

"You are their leader? They listen to you?"

"Yes. They called me the Prophet."

"That is good, brother. I am pleased to see you this way. I shall dwell with you for a time, if I am welcome."

"Most welcome, Tecumseh." Laulewasika smiled oddly and closed his good eye, as if lost in a private meditation about the holy roads. Tecumseh rose quietly and stole out.

During the weeks that followed, Tecumseh realized that Laulewasika did indeed exert a powerful hold over the followers he had gathered in the quiet green glen on the White River's banks. Laulewasika frequently had dreams, and he recited them to his followers. It was not long before he announced that the Great Spirit had whispered in a dream that he should found a holy village in the Ohio lands.

"What is your opinion of this matter, Tecumseh?" asked Iron Horns, a young, lithe, though rather fanatic-eyed Delaware who had joined the Prophet's village several months earlier. He, Tecumseh, the Prophet and several other important warriors of the small town had seated themselves in the crudely built council house to discuss the vision.

Tecumseh glanced from one face to another. Clearly all but his brother waited for his decision.

"I do not think it wise for you to return to the Ohio country," he began. "The Long Knives are many."

"Would you deny me the truth of my vision?" Laulewasika exclaimed. "My followers believe with me in the power of the Great Spirit."

Still Tecumseh could see the others watching for his reaction. He could sway them if he wished. Yet the religious fervor his brother had generated was a good force, and Tecumseh quickly grasped that it needed to be nourished, for one day it might be useful as a rallying point for the tribes. To weaken its strength now might be worse than the dangers of the Prophet braving a return to the Ohio lands. In any case, he knew the decision lay with him, for the wisdom of his thoughts and the power of his leadership on the frontier was strong enough to override, if necessary, even loyalty to the Prophet.

"I will bow to the will of the Great Spirit," Tecumseh announced. A smile crossed the Prophet's face and the others in the group smiled also.

So Laulewasika and his ragtag band of poverty-stricken followers migrated back toward Ohio.

November, 1805, brought unusually warm weather, and Laulewasika's newly settled village on Greenville Creek looked almost prosperous in the crisp sunlight as Tecumseh, who had been away on a hunting trip, saw it for the first time. A log meetinghouse had been erected, and around this central building stood more than half a hundred wigwams and cabins. Tecumseh noted with pleasure that the people in the village appeared happy and industrious, putting aside the last joints of meat, hung up in a long bark-sided house, that would supply them through the winter. Not a single warrior sotted with Yankee whisky could be seen anywhere. This was indeed a good sign.

"I greet you, my brother Laulewasika," Tecumseh said when he joined the younger man in the council house.

Dreamily the younger man shook his head. "I am Tenskwautawa."

"Are you joking with me, brother?"

"I am not. That is the name I have taken."

"How come you to choose this name which means the Open Door?"

Quietly, the younger man answered, "Because the Jesus of the whites said, '*I am the door*.' The Shakers read it to me from their holy book. Weeks ago I learned that Change of Feathers, the prophet of the Shawnee, was dead. When I heard, I grew faint and everything became dark. I awoke with the new name burned into my mind. Shall you lodge with us long, my brother?"

"A while," Tecumseh mused. He intended to remain in Greenville until he learned just how widespread was his brother's new influence over his followers.

Some idea of Tenskwautawa's growing leadership came to Tecumseh that night as he sat on the edge of a crowd of villagers gathered for evening devotions. The sun dipped low in Greenville Creek, turning it molten red, and the scrap of cloth covering the eye of the Prophet fluttered lightly in the twilight breeze.

Every face turned upward to listen while Tecumseh's brother spoke.

"We are Shawnee and we must remain Shawnee!" Tenskwautawa raised his arms and spread them wide, silhouetted against the reddening night sky. "Become Shawnee again, my brethren," Tenskwautawa shouted, and you shall rule this land forever!"

People surged to their feet in a frenzy of enthusiasm.

Tecumseh's brain sang with hope. Could it be possible that his own brother would be the one to help him gather all the tribes into a single great force, to remove forever the whites from their land? The Open Door had indeed become a leader. With Tecumseh at his side, there might be no limit to their success!

8.

. . . AND THE SUN WENT OUT

Tecumseh stirred restlessly. Above the sound of birds chattering there arose a new commotion. His body became taut upon the deer robe where he had been sleeping. In an instant he blinked the last trance of weariness from his eyes and crawled slowly to his feet. He listened carefully to the excited voices outside the wigwam, until he was certain. Yes, one voice had risen briefly above the others, speaking in the tongue of the white man.

Darting from the wigwam, Tecumseh kept his hand firmly upon his tomahawk. Then he saw the head of the white man bobbing above the crowd before the log meetinghouse. Grimly he moved in that direction. Tenskwautawa threw his brother an apprehensive glance from the center of the throng. Tecumseh halted at the fringe of the crowd to listen.

". . . and thus I bring this message from William Henry Harrison," the white scout spoke. His tanned face turned a shade paler when he recognized Tecumseh, but he went on in fluent Shawnee: "Harrison is the powerful governor of the Indiana Territory. He has sent me from his wigwam at Vincennes because he wishes to be the friend of the Shawnee and Delaware. He does not want them to listen to false prophets."

"Which one does the sachem Harrison call false?" Tecumseh shouted. His voice turned many heads. A respectful path opened through the disturbed crowd.

The white scout, hardly more than twenty, wiped a buckskin sleeve across his perspiring lips and tried to face Tecumseh boldly. The scout pointed to Tecumseh's brother. "This one, the brother of Tecumseh, is a false prophet. That is my message from the governor."

Instantly Tecumseh sensed the plot and the danger. Early in the year, news had reached him of Harrison's fear of the Prophet's growing power, and he suspected the scout's message was part of a clever attempt to discredit his brother. That must not happen!

"The sachem Harrison has a crooked tongue when he speaks so," Tecumseh replied. "The Shawnee and Delaware believe in the way of the Prophet."

Even as he spoke, here and there in the crowd a doubtful eye turned away, an uncertain head shook in a puzzled fashion. Harrison, too, represented strength on the frontier. A cloud passed before the sun, and the crowd fell into shadow for a moment. The scout glanced around, whipped up his arm and pointed.

"The governor Harrison tells his friends that if the Prophet is truly a holy man, he should be willing to perform miracles to show his holy nature. While the governor does not believe he can perform miracles, he asks that he do so, in order that the Shawnee may see who is their true friend—Harrison or the Man-With-One-Eye." An uneasy but satisfied smile flicked across the scout's face. He thought he had won a victory. A restless muttering ran through the crowd. The cloud disappeared from the sun, but the Prophet shivered and huddled in the shadow of the meetinghouse.

Tecumseh's voice hardened. "Return to your sachem," he said to the scout. "You have given us your message."

"That'll be a pure pleasure, ladies and gents," the scout said in English. A rather amused expression crinkled his lips as he touched his cap in mock politeness and hefted his long rifle. Then he mounted his pony and clattered away.

The crowd broke up quickly. The Prophet uttered feeble requests for a hearing, but suspicion could rise suddenly in the minds of the villagers. Tecumseh sensed it had already taken root, and if not rapidly cut down, it might grow to damaging proportions. Above all, that must not happen now. The time was coming when his great plan might at last be put into effect.

"That evil Harrison has destroyed all my work!" Tenskwautawa cried shrilly. "Today my people call me the Prophet, but what sort of prophet shall I be if the white leader hurls insults—"

"Be still!" Tecumseh snapped.

"But my brother knows I can work no miracles, and yet in a few moments I have lost the faith of all my people."

"That is because they will listen to you only while no stronger voice speaks. You must answer the sachem Harrison and smash the words back into his teeth."

"With what?" Tenskwautawa wailed.

Tecumseh smiled slowly. "Why, with a miracle."

"A miracle?" The Prophet blinked in the cool shadows. "Are you mad?"

"No. I dislike trickery. I curse it, yet I have much at stake—the plan of which I spoke. I shall not lose you as my ally. Therefore. . ." He seized the Prophet's wrist. "Your hand shall darken the sun." Tecumseh's eyes blazed. "This very hand!"

Tenskwautawa shook his head miserably. "There is no way. . ."

"Call warriors. There must be many feet running tonight, for words of the Prophet's coming miracle shall travel to every corner of the land where the tribes dwell." Seeing his brother's disbelief, Tecumseh cried sharply, "Call them, I say! At once, now!"

Shaking his head miserably, the strange figure of the Prophet shambled away from the meetinghouse toward a group of braves gathered by another wigwam. Tecumseh watched the spectacle of suspicion. Faces which had been friendly at dawn now turned to stare at the Prophet with open distrust. Sadly Tecumseh recognized that this was the way of all the tribes. They were quick as summer lightning in their emotions. His plan *must* work.

The morning was the sixteenth, in the month of June. The runners and the smoke columns had told the story well: On this morning the Prophet would blacken the sun.

By ten-thirty the entire village had assembled on the fringe of Greenville Creek. Children scuffled, old toothless women chattered busily, a yellow dog yapped at the water's edge. It was a piercingly clear day, without a spot of cloud to mar the blue sky. Tecumseh squatted near the edge of the throng, worried that something would go wrong at the last moment.

Almost as though it came from one giant throat, a sigh rose from the crowd.

Up the creek bank the Prophet had stepped from his wigwam, his head adorned with a plume of ebony raven wings. He moved slowly and impressively along the bank, his black robes rustling around his moccasined feet. He stopped, raised both arms dramatically above his head and cried:

"I am the Prophet. You shall believe in me. This day I shall blot out the sun!"

Abruptly he sat down on a stump and peered at the sky. Tecumseh was glad that he had coached his brother, for he knew that Tenskwautawa was trembling with uncertainty.

The crowd continued talking restlessly until nearly an hour passed. Tecumseh felt perspiration trickling down his spine beneath his hide shirt. Very slowly he nodded. The Prophet caught the signal, rose and flung his hand at the sun, pointing.

Every voice along the creek bank went silent.

"The sun shall darken, because the Prophet speaks!"

Tenskwautawa's arm began to tremble, held aloft for another few seconds while nothing happened. Then there was a shrill feminine scream. Tecumseh spun around. A young woman had fainted. Tecumseh whirled once more—and there was a dark, mysterious stain upon the edge of the sun!

Darkness crept very slowly across the face of the sun, until at last the great burning eye of light was an eerie gray ball suspended overhead. All tension left Tecumseh suddenly. He had won his fight, but only with the help of the eclipse whose coming had been known to nearly every educated white man on the frontier. The date, the exact time—all this had been predicted. All this Tecumseh had heard of months before, far over in Springfield, in the Illinois lands, where whites from a great place of learning called Harvard were already working to set up their telescopes in order to see the moon pass across the sun's face.

"*The sun shall glow once more*!" Tenskwautawa cried. "*The Prophet speaks!*"

And at one edge of the sun a line of intense, eye-hurting fire began to burn.

When the sun shone again, the crowd crept silently away. Many stole forward to touch the hem of the Prophet's robe. Only Tecumseh stood aloof, sad now that the spectacle was finished, for it had been a trick. Yet the moment was coming when he would need his people's faith in the Prophet. He hoped sorrowfully that the Great Spirit—*and* the Shawnee—might one day forgive him his deceit, when they realized he had committed it only so that a greater good might be brought about.

He moved forward along the bank of Greenville Creek to where the Prophet waited, black robes flapping, raven's plume tossing, eye patch blowing in the wind, a strange, suddenly terrible figure of magic and power.

"Send the runners," Tecumseh said simply. "Tell of the miracle. After three suns, you and I shall follow. The hour of uniting is here."

In the sudden burst of humid weather which descended during the next three days, Tecumseh and the Prophet slept little. Through the steaming nights they remained awake, summoning warriors before them, assigning each a direction in which to travel, presenting to each an ornate wampum belt made partially of dried beans. These beans had special significance, and the Prophet was careful to instruct each messenger in the purpose of the belt. Whoever touched the bean belt would be touching the hand of the Prophet, for the beans belonged to him. To touch the belt was to become the Prophet's sworn kinsman. At the end of these three exhausting days and nights, with the village nearly deserted of young men, Tecumseh and the Prophet rode forth on ponies of their own.

Westward they rode in the summer's furious heat. In the first Miami village they were welcomed by all the people, who drew back and peered at the Prophet with awe, even with fright. Purposely Tecumseh kept himself in the background.

Gathered in the sachem's wigwam that evening were the leaders of the Miami village. Chief among these was a frail, white-haired brave whose eyes sparkled blackly as he wheezed to the Prophet:

"We saw the sun go out, O Tenskwautawa, and we longed to hear words from your lips, for truly we realized you were a holy man."

Tecumseh watched with satisfaction as his brother smiled dreamily into the firelight. "It is good to know that you trust my tongue as one which is straight. The spirits which dwell in the sky demand that we live as brothers if we are to regain the heritage which belongs to us."

"Tell us, O Prophet, what path we must travel to follow you?"

"First you must abandon the evil whisky of the white man. Second you must kill your dogs. Third you must cast aside your medicine bags, your herbs, your charms, your magic spells and remedies. Fourth. . ."

The white-haired old Miami, toothless but bright eyed, leaned forward listening intently as the Prophet monotonously recited his odd catalog of restrictions and rules. Tecumseh's mind pulled inward upon itself, so that he could think his own thoughts without listening to the voice of his brother. Of what value was killing a dog or casting aside a medicine bag, except as part of the new ritual of the Prophet? The details mattered little to Tecumseh. It was the goal behind the prophet's activities which staggered his brain, set it on fire with a bright blazing hope for his people.

At last Tecumseh believed he had found the answer to the miseries of all the tribes who were being crushed beneath the grinding wagon wheels of the settlers coming to claim the land. There was one way—a way Joseph Brant had first named:

To forge all tribes into one tribe.

To bind every tribe into a single tribe with a single purpose —resistance.

To create upon the wild face of the frontier an army of warriors so huge, so powerful, they would outnumber the Long Knives as the leaves outnumbered the trunks of trees. To have not a thousand small groups of warriors fighting the whites, not a hundred tribes, but a single army, one great confederation, under one leader. One mighty force of red men from every corner of the continent, rising up if necessary, to smite the Long Knives so that they would retreat back to their cities and forever remain there.

This, Tecumseh knew at last, in the steamy little wigwam where Tenskwautawa prattled to the senile old Miami sachem, was his purpose, his destiny. He now recognized his own role as a leader. He had already passed thirty-eight summers, and stood at the peak of his physical and mental strength, ready for the supreme effort. Unite the tribes—for peace *or* war! Make them all brothers against the white man! It would take much work, much talk, much force perhaps, yet his mind was fired with the notion that it *could* be accomplished. Brant's confederation of the eastern tribes and upper New York had never met with any great success, but Tecumseh felt that he was a leader powerful enough to complete the task, beginning with the Indians of his own land.

The Prophet had provided him with the first means of entry into the hearts of the stubborn warriors who prized loyalty to their own tribes above all else. The code of renunciation of the white man's ways, though it was confused with many odd rules born of the Prophet's strange mind, was still the first step toward bringing all red men on the continent into a single great force.

". . . and thus if your people shall follow my ways," Tenskwautawa was finishing, "they shall find their old wisdom restored."

And if they follow me, Tecumseh thought, *they shall find the land restored and they shall rule.*

The summer seemed to quicken. Tecumseh and the Prophet were constantly moving, riding, stopping to council with a village for an hour, journeying along big creeks and small rivers in their canoe. And as they gathered followers, so did the warriors who had gone out from Greenville with the bean belts, for each messenger repeated the Prophet's instructions. All who listened touched the bean belts.

Tecumseh and Tenskwautawa soon split along different trails. Stories filtered through the Indiana frontier of the Prophet's rising zeal. Here and there a warrior spoke against the new doctrine. The Prophet was traveling with a band of his own loyal followers who plunged knives into the hearts of the few who dared speak against him. These foolish ones were condemned as victims of evil spirits, men inhabited by demons.

The reports of fanatic slaughter displeased Tecumseh. He did not find it necessary to employ such tactics. But he realized that as days passed, the Prophet grew more emotional, more mystical, more firmly caught by the notion he himself had created, that he was a savior. The killings also reinforced Tecumseh's belief that when the time came it would be he, not the Prophet, who must step to the head of the great force representing all the tribes. Tecumseh, who had prepared, whose head was cool, whose mind was sharp.

But meanwhile, the year 1807 slipped upon them, with talk of a great war. And all along the frontier the bean belts were passing, and thousands touched the symbolic Prophet's hand, joining him, gathering together.

9. THE GREAT JOURNEY

)n the twenty-second day of the month of June, 1807, in the ·oastal waters off the state of Virginia, a United States frigate ıauled down her colors—and the sparks that would set a land ›n fire with war blew hot.

She was the *Chesapeake.* She should have been carrying fifty ;uns. Because she did not, the *Leopard* closed in, and the flag ame down. The *Chesapeake's* men were forced to surrender to he crew of the British man-of-war, and were forced into British ervice. The American coast was closed to all British warships ›y the orders of President Thomas Jefferson. And in the Ken-ucky House of Representatives, the stormy voice of the war ıawk Henry Clay began to rise, demanding that the British with-lraw their forces completely from the American continent. \bove the Great Lakes a formidable British army was gar-·isoned, waiting. For what? the Yankees wondered. War talk vas spreading across the frontier. War with George III, the Great King. War with England. War coming. *War!*

While the frontier seethed, while the white settlers argued ınd speculated, Tecumseh sat at Greenville—listening, watch-ng, planning.

One starry April evening in 1808, Tecumseh called Tens-:wautawa to his wigwam. He came quickly when summoned.)ull cherry-red embers were dying. Long shadows lay on either side of Tecumseh's nose and below his eyes. Outside, the Ohio earth smelled wet and black, growing alive with a buzz of spring insects. Tenskwautawa peered at his brother who stared into the fire. In Tecumseh's mind was the image of a fair face. Rebecca. . .

The Prophet tugged uneasily at the handkerchief covering his ruined eye, for he sensed his brother's moodiness.

Tecumseh inhaled deeply, closed his eyes a moment, then straightened.

"We wait no longer, Tenskwautawa. The sky is growing dark for war. Soon the Long Knives and the soldiers of the Great King shall fight. That will be the opportunity." Tecumseh's eyes glittered in the last pop of the fiery embers. "Perhaps our only opportunity. We must form the confederation of the tribes now. I have a task for you."

"What is that?"

"When the sun rises, gather braves and march to the British at Fort Malden, at the mouth of the Detroit River. Ask whether the Great King will be our ally if the tribes rise against the Long Knives."

Nervously the Prophet passed a hand across his mouth. "You —you think the time has come at last?"

Tecumseh nodded slowly. "Tonight I feel strangely weary in all of my bones, as though I shall never sleep peacefully or rest fully again. I am forty summers, yet I feel my life begins only now. Perhaps I do not wish it to begin in this way. I think I would rather be lazy and sleep in the sunlight and net fish and hunt. But it can be no other way."

For a long moment the Prophet said nothing. Then his lips opened to question Tecumseh's instructions, but no sound came. Sitting perfectly still in the last ember light, Tecumseh truly seemed a hard bronze statue staring at nothing and everything, thinking thoughts of such scope that the Prophet was frightened because he was a lesser man and could not understand.

Tenskwautawa slipped out, murmuring, "It shall be done as you say."

But cannon were thundering on the distant earth of Europe, and George III was engaged most seriously with the Corsican Napoleon Bonaparte. The Prophet returned with his party from Malden, the British fort which stood at Amherstburg, Ontario, Canada, having received a less than friendly welcome from the British. They were too concerned with the results of the European war to enter alliances with red savages for a war which, fortunately, had not yet begun. The Prophet reported the rejection and confessed he did not fathom the military and diplomatic principles involved. Tecumseh grasped them all too well. Because the Great King was not ready to join with the tribes, Tecumseh's effort would be more difficult, but by no means impossible.

When Tecumseh next called the Prophet to him, the younger brother understood the instructions even less.

"Abandon this village of Greenville?" Tenskwautawa exclaimed. "This is my holy city, founded from orders given me in a vision."

The Prophet had brought with him a small group of followers who muttered angrily in agreement with his words.

Tecumseh swept the gathering with a hard gaze. "Evidently you are not aware that night and day the eyes of the Long Knives watch us. There are too many of them in this land now. We must be free to move without being spied upon. And you have told me that provisions for the villagers are already growing scarce. The Long Knives take the game from the forest. Very well. The Potawatomi have offered us land along the Tippecanoe. Upon that tract we shall build a new holy city."

"No!" cried one of the group. "It is not right, not fitting that. . ."

Tecumseh stared steadily at the warrior. At last the warrior looked away and Tecumseh said, "Are there others of you who would dispute my word?"

Silence. Then someone in the group grumbled.

"Speak!" Tecumseh demanded. "Or obey."

Not a sound disturbed the scene for several moments. Tecumseh's face relaxed then, and he laid a friendly hand on his brother's shoulder. "We shall name the new village Prophet's Town, in your honor. And it shall be greater far than this Greenville, for in the Prophet's Town we shall sow the seeds of the confederation."

During April and May of the year 1808 Tenskwautawa and his followers migrated overland to the west bank of Indiana's Tippecanoe River land, which extended along the river to its point of joining with the Wabash. The Prophet traveled with eighty families. In May they raised the new village, with houses of logs, with wigwams and with a mission building in which he preached.

There, as the village rose in the Indiana forest, Tecumseh spoke to his brother of the journey he had planned:

"While you build our city, I go to meet the tribes. I shall be gone a long time, but when I return I hope that clasped in my hand will be the pledges of the other tribes. We must gather all our brethren into one single army, so that when the war clouds burst we are ready to bargain or fight. That shall be my task—to present the plan, to win support for it. I have summoned Sauganash, who shall go with me, together with a party of braves."

Full summer spread its heat and its rioting green along the Tippecanoe as Tecumseh arrayed himself in his simplest, finest apparel—the buckskin jacket with the silver-hilted hunting knife at his belt, and the hollow pipestone tomahawk, through which might be sucked the smoke of the peace fire. The entire populace of the raw new village of Prophet's Town assembled to bid him farewell, with Tenskwautawa in his black robes chanting a prayer for his brother's success.

Tecumseh touched his knees lightly to his pony and jogged forward. Sauganash—"The Britisher," as he was known to the Indians—followed rapidly on horseback, catching up as Tecumseh made his way along the sparkling riverbank. With a smile on his freckled face, Sauganash—whose Christian name was Billy Caldwell—said:

"Many miles to travel, eh, Brother Tecumseh?"

A lonely smile touched the Shawnee's mouth. "Hard miles. If only they will listen to my words, heed my plan!"

Caldwell nodded hopefully. "They will listen. Every tongue is silent when Tecumseh speaks."

"Let us hope it is so." And with that he urged his mount into a gallop.

Westward they rode, toward Illinois, Tecumseh, his guard of handsome young braves and Billy Caldwell, the half-breed son of an Irishman and the Shawnee sister of Chief Blue Jacket. The boy had been reared by the Jesuit fathers of Detroit. He spoke the languages of Europe and most of the tribal dialects as well, and for many years, more Shawnee than white, he had been known as a dangerous foe of the whites along the frontier. Caldwell was a fighter, which the Prophet was not. Tecumseh had summoned him from a great distance, because the idea of a union of all tribes might very well be met with not only spoken displeasure but with armed resistance. Should there be fighting . . . well, Caldwell's arrows flew swiftly—and straight.

In the Potawatomi villages along the Illinois River, Tecumseh faced his first test. Many braves were gathered in the council house ruled by Topinabee, a strong, wise sachem. Tecumseh rose and quietly began to speak. At first the younger bloods in the council house smiled occasionally, stirring where they sat. Then a fierce glance from Topinabee quieted them. Tecumseh found the words coming fluently to his tongue, rich, persuasive:

"My brethren, I think you know that I am a reasonable man, and thus you will not believe me foolish if at first I ask you to think of a single blade of grass. Imagine it well, this thin, single blade standing alone in a vast field of rock, and when the picture is fixed firmly in your heads, imagine yourself upon a fleet pony coming upon this single blade and trampling it. An easy task, a simple task, is it not?

"But now consider that same blade multiplied by ten thousand, and then again by ten thousand, and still again and again, until there stands not one blade in the wind but an endless field. Then picture yourself, your pony, trying to trample all that great field; bringing up more ponies, an army of ponies. Still you could not trample down all the blades of the field. Still many would remain standing upright in the sun.

"So I would have you believe it is with the tribes of our race. One tribe alone against the Long Knives can be crushed. Ten tribes as one can resist. Twenty tribes as one can conquer.

"For unless we join together to regain the land which has already been taken from us—and the land which will yet be taken from us unless we fight—we shall all be driven from these lands. And time is escaping, my brethren, for war is coming as surely as a great red ball of light arose in the eastern heavens this morning and will rise there tomorrow morning and for countless mornings until the world's end."

All through his speech Tecumseh had noted the burning intensity with which one of the younger warriors watched him. The man had fierce black eyes and was perhaps thirty summers or slightly more. Tecumseh instantly liked the young man's splendid physique, coupled with his firm yet reasonable expression. He took pains to direct some of his words to this unknown warrior who was seated on Topinabee's right, indicating a position of influence among the Potawatomi. As Tecumseh finished, and before Topinabee could frame a reply or a comment, the younger man climbed to his feet.

"My father and my comrades," he said swiftly, "my blood quickens at the words of our Shawnee brother. He speaks great truth."

Topinabee smiled tolerantly. "Chief Tecumseh, he who speaks is Shabbona. Though born an Ottawa, he resides among us as the husband of my daughter."

"I am pleased that Shabbona has received my message with good heart," Tecumseh said.

"His feelings are mine," Topinabee replied. "Your plan is a good one. You must stay with us a while so that we may talk more of it." Topinabee's regal gaze swept the council house. "I do not hesitate to say that those warriors of the Potawatomi loyal to me shall be loyal to you if war comes. Your signal to arms shall be ours."

Flushed with the triumph of this first conversion, Tecumseh merely bowed his head in acknowledgment. A moment later he said:

"While I would like to dwell with Topinabee and his people for many days, I cannot. There are many other tribes which I must visit quickly, for time grows short. Already the soldiers of the Great King at Malden practice the drills of warfare."

Shabbona turned intently to his father-in-law. "Let me ride with Tecumseh to the other tribes, so that I may speak for the Potawatomi."

Topinabee frowned. "You believe so ardently that you would leave your wife and your children?"

Shabbona gave a quick nod. "If no tribe is safe from the invasion of the Long Knives, neither are my mate and my little ones."

"Then go with my full approval, Shabbona, if it is agreeable to our Shawnee brother."

"I would welcome Shabbona beside me," Tecumseh answered, strangely touched. He felt that in the young Ottawa he had found another man who sensed the scope of his own vision and was eager to carry it out. "We ride north."

Shabbona's eyes shone. "I shall be ready."

And so it was that Shabbona of the Potawatomi went with Tecumseh and his braves to the Wisconsin lands, to the dwelling places of the Sauk.

Night after night in stuffy council houses Tecumseh gathered his strength and stood alone hour after hour, pleading, persuading, now quietly, now with a thundering voice, every moment holding aloft the bright dream of a single battle standard under which all the tribes might unite.

White Cedar and Keokuk, sachems of the Sauk, doubted the wisdom of his plan. But as he had found Shabbona among the Potawatomi, he found an ally in Black Hawk the village chief among the Sauk, and moving east again across the Wisconsin lands to the villages of the Winnebago, he felt he had scored a partial victory with the tribe. Black Hawk had pledged bands of young braves to his support.

Along the shores of the beautiful blue Lake Michigan, the chiefs Naw Kaw and Four Legs pledged the Winnebago to war. Tecumseh moved south, the long journey only just begun.

On the eastern bank of the great Wabash he won the Kickapoo to his cause. And traveling back home again toward Ohio country, he won a number of the Wyandot also, the young warriors pledging for war in spite of the resistance of their aging chief, The Crane.

South, then, with Billy Caldwell, with Shabbona and his small party—thousands of miles—to the Seminole of Florida. Back across the sprawling yellow Mississippi to the lands of the savage Osage on the Arkansas River.

Pitch pine torches smoldered, filling the interior of the Osage council lodge with acrid smoke as Tecumseh stood in the center of a ring of impassive faces. Even as his speech sped steadily to its thundering conclusion, he could see—dismally—that the expression of River Pole, the aging Osage chieftain who sat huddled in his gaudy scarlet trade blanket, was far from friendly. Choking back his sense of frustration, Tecumseh raised his voice:

"My argument is the argument of truth. The Osage are wise men, and River Pole is a wise sachem. I pray to the Great Spirit that they will see the truth. The Long Knives use cheating and trickery to seize our lands. Their treaty papers are no more than tricks, to be signed with smiles one summer and forgotten the next—when the Long Knives hunger for lands beyond the treaty line. The truth, O brethren, lies in the fact that only as one nation of red men are we mighty. Only as one powerful confederation can we conquer. Tribe by tribe, alone, there is but one fate for us."

Tecumseh's eyes swept the throng.

"Recognize this truth most of all, brethren of the Osage. Alone, there is but one fate—that we shall perish."

Long, agonized moments passed. The pitch pine torches smoked. At last River Pole grunted:

"No. The war is far away. The Osage are at peace. No."

"*No . . . no . . . no.*" The word went around the council lodge, from mouth to mouth, grumbled at first, then spoken, then shouted. Tecumseh stood iron straight, not daring to move for fear of showing his disappointment. It took all his courage to remain overnight with River Pole's people. When he put the village of the Osage behind him next morning, there was a dismal sadness in his heart.

The year 1809 found Tecumseh riding into the camps of the Iroquois, in distant New York. Though Joseph Brant was dead now, Tecumseh felt that he was repaying the visit which the great Mohawk had made to his land in 1781. But from the Iroquois he received rejection again, a stubborn refusal to give up their position as a single tribe and blend themselves into a gigantic army.

So Tecumseh turned west once more as the fall settled on the frontier. He had won a measure of success on the early parts of the great journey. Each day brought war closer. And while his triumph had not been complete, he *had* found followers who would fight.

On a brilliant fall evening in 1809, just after the weary party had crossed into the Indiana lands, coming at last to the end of a gigantic journey which had lasted more than a year, Tecumseh's successes were smashed by bitter news.

Shabbona came galloping back along the sun-dappled trail with an unfamiliar warrior riding behind. The two men pulled up. The messenger gazed unhappily at Tecumseh. He identified himself, then spoke:

"I was sent by your brother the Prophet to spy upon the Long Knives at Fort Wayne. Ever since the paper was signed there, we have been on the trails day and night seeking you, for the messages said you were returning."

"Fort Wayne?" Tecumseh's face drained of color. "Paper? What paper?"

The warrior bowed his head before the horrifying ferocity of Tecumseh's mounting anger. "A new treaty." The words touched Tecumseh's mind like a knife. "New lands have already been given to the Long Knives."

"By whom?" Tecumseh whispered.

"By the Delaware, and by the Miami and by. . ."

But Tecumseh had already lashed his pony around the messenger. Shabbona shouted hoarsely. The party of warriors leaped ahead, following Tecumseh as he thundered wrathfully along the trail to Prophet's Town.

10.
THE CHALLENGE OF THE SALT

Seated with his brother and half a dozen Shawnee spies who had watched the treaty-making at Fort Wayne, Tecumseh heard the tale of betrayal. Tension hung in the air at Prophet's Town. The inhabitants had seen him ride furiously into the village with his brow black as a storm. Never before had they witnessed his rage at such a high peak.

Governor Harrison, the spies reported, had departed from the city of Vincennes on the first day of September.

"Knowing full well that I was not here and could not speak for my people!" Tecumseh raged.

"Fifteen days later," the spy continued, "the white sachem arrived at Fort Wayne. He did not call men of all the tribes. That," the spy added, "was part of his plot."

"How many were there?" Tecumseh asked quietly.

"Thirteen hundred or more. Delaware, Miami, Potawatomi, the Eel River tribe. . ."

Tecumseh spat upon the ground. "But did the white Harrison call for a single Shawnee?"

The spy shook his head.

"Or a single Wea? A single Kickapoo? Yet we are also the dwellers upon the stolen land!"

Uncertainly the spy continued: "At last the sachem Little Turtle, who is old and sick, arrived on the twenty-second day and the meetings commenced. The governor Harrison said that he wished more land for the Long Knives, land to the eastern side of the Wabash. Only with this land could the whites of the Indiana country form a state, as was the desire of the Great White Father. There was much talk of the good fortune the tribes would enjoy when paid money for the land. Harrison said we would live better lives if we would cultivate the soil. He said that we should give up hunting, because the great war far away across the sea has made the furs we trap of little worth.

"There was a map brought before the sachems, but few understood its meaning," he went on. They cried instead for the liquor casks to be smashed open. When this was done, all resistance to Harrison's plan was forgotten. The sachem Winimac of the Potawatomi pledged the support of the tribes, and then the paper was signed."

Now Tecumseh's face twisted in even deeper fury. "*Winimac* dared to speak for Tecumseh and his people? Winimac shall answer for presuming to sell away for cheap coin the land which does not belong to him."

Gradually Tecumseh learned the rest of the bitter story. Three million acres of land had been sold to the white men, at a price of little more than ten thousand dollars. Rapidly Tecumseh calculated. He knew well that the American government charged settlers two dollars per acre for such land, and he was able to estimate the almost staggering profit which the whites had made upon signing the treaty. To the insult of ignoring the Shawnee had been added the crime of gross thievery. Harrison had victimized the tribes and made them suffer because of their pitiful ignorance of legal methods.

Tecumseh glanced at his younger brother.

"The whites have taken the country of the Beautiful River from us, and if they push us back to the other side of the Wabash, we are doomed. We shall not cross. We shall keep this land, even though. . ." He hesitated, as if unwilling to voice the words which he knew were truth: ". . . even though we must go to war."

The Prophet frowned unhappily. "Must we always be the ones to speak first of war?"

Tecumseh said, "They have given us no choice."

He mustered his forces that winter. Then further fuel was stoked on the fire of his anger when Governor Harrison signed an additional treaty with the Kickapoo tribe, purchasing still more land.

When the bluish ice in the Tippecanoe River cracked with spring and the green buds of the sycamores burst their winter shells, Prophet's Town was no longer a village of peaceful souls dedicated only to religion. There were more than a thousand warriors camped there. Spies to the north reported regularly on British activities at Fort Malden. The forest around the village rang with the sound of hunting forays which became mock battles as the braves prepared themselves for war. Tecumseh led his men in battle drills, teaching them how to advance and retreat in orderly fashion. The hands of the women and the younger men worked feverishly all day long, hammering and chiseling bits of stone. They were making arrowheads along the Tippecanoe.

One hot June morning Tecumseh was moving down the Wabash with a band of hunters which included a Frenchman named Michael Brouillette, a trader who had come to Prophet's Town in April. Brouillette was a thin, unpleasant sort, with sallow skin and shaggy black hair. His buckskins were greasy and stained and he walked in a permanent slouch, scuffing his moccasins and peering out at the world with watery gray eyes. That morning Tecumseh had grudgingly agreed to let him join the party, since Brouillette was very nearly out of beads, blankets and other trade goods, and found little to occupy himself in the village. Now the Frenchman slouched along through the brush, halting suddenly and squinting in the direction of the river.

"Eh, listen, Chief Tecumseh!" he said in ragged Shawnee. "Down by the shore, a racket and a rattling. You hear?"

Tecumseh had already cupped his hands about his mouth. He gave a soft, piping whippoorwill cry. It was echoed eerily from the Wabash. Tecumseh signaled again. Quiet as ghosts, nearly a dozen armed braves converged from the green of the forest and stood before their leader. Another warrior padded swiftly toward the group from the direction of the shore.

"There is a flatboat of the whites coming up the water," the brave reported.

Tecumseh's mouth hardened. "Come. We shall meet them."

Silently the warriors fanned out through the thickets. Brouillette hung back for a moment, saw Tecumseh watching him and shuffled to catch up. Within moments Tecumseh was crouched behind a screen of brush above the sandy shore. He spied the flatboat in midstream with four husky men aboard, and signaled with his hand. His braves broke from cover, long rifles lifted. One of the boatmen shouted in surprise. A few swift maneuvers of the poles and the flatboat nosed into shore.

The boatmen lined up along the rail, all of them grinning amiably enough. One clearly recognized Tecumseh, for he pointed and spoke to a comrade about him. The flatboat grounded with a crunch. Aboard were several high stacks of wooden kegs.

Tecumseh stepped forward and identified himself. "Why have you come?"

"My name is Jenks," said one of the young men. "These other fellows are French, and we were sent up the Wabash to deliver these barrels of salt to Prophet's Town."

"Who sent you?" Tecumseh demanded.

"Why, Harrison. This salt is for the Kickapoos who signed the treaty a month or so back."

Tecumseh's eyes grew threatening. He touched his tomahawk. "I rule Prophet's Town and I will not accept the kegs. Take them back to your Harrison at Vincennes and say Tecumseh refuses."

Jenks exclaimed in English, "Well, strip my hide and. . . !" Then, perplexed, he turned to his comrades and conversed in French. An excited babbling broke out among the boatmen. At last Jenks scratched his chest and shook his head.

"I can't see much reason for your turning down the salt. Afraid we'll have to dump it off right here, like our orders say."

With a leap Tecumseh mounted the rail of the flatboat. Jenks cried out sharply. Tecumseh's arm whipped up, then down. The blade of his tomahawk split the head of one of the casks. The white crystalline salt spilled out on the damp deck planking. Tecumseh whirled around.

"Tell your Harrison I do not accept his salt because I do not accept his treaties which steal our land—and I am the leader!"

Jenks scowled. "Now wait a second."

Then he licked his lips. There were ten long rifles aimed at him along the shore. Jenks sighed and shrugged. Tecumseh hefted his tomahawk, turned and jumped down to the sand. In that instant he saw Brouillette raise his hand, trying to conceal a signal to one of the boatmen.

Instantly Tecumseh had his tomahawk at Brouillette's throat. Two other warriors gripped the trader's arms. Brouillette's brow grew damp with sweat as Tecumseh said in a low, piercing whisper:

"White man, you told us you came from the Canadian lands. How is it, then, that you make signs to the men on the boat? How is it that you know Long Knives from Vincennes?"

"I. . . I met. . ." Brouillette began weakly.

The keen edge of Tecumseh's tomahawk drew a thin, glistening line of blood.

"The truth is what I wish from your lips. Were you sent to Prophet's Town to spy?"

Brouillette shivered. Then he nodded.

"By the governor Harrison?"

"Yes, but. . ."

Roughly Tecumseh caught Brouillette by the scruff of the collar and flung him toward the flatboat. Jenks reached down to help him aboard. The other boatmen jumped to the poles to set the boat adrift again. Tecumseh stalked down the sand, tall and proud and savage, staring coldly at the Long Knives.

"You may tell your Harrison that next time he should send a man for a spy, not a feeble snake. Take your boat from my river, before my anger grows too strong. We are the owners of these lands, not Harrison." Tecumseh's tomahawk glittered in the air as he swung it in a savage, threatening arc. "Get away!"

The shaken Brouillette leaped to man a pole, as did Jenks, and in a few moments the flatboat was gone around a bend of the sunlit Wabash.

Tecumseh's challenge was not long unanswered. Within a month, word drifted up the Wabash that Harrison was sending a messenger with a letter. Since the incident with Brouillette, Tecumseh had been busy tightening his defense lines about Prophet's Town. He wanted no further reports on the size of his forces to reach Vincennes. Thus the messenger, a young American named Joseph Barron, who arrived in late July, was seized on the river and escorted under guard into the village. A crowd gathered near the meetinghouse, where the Prophet sat in a large, elaborately carved wooden chair upon a platform. He was an imposing figure in his black robes, with the silk handkerchief across his ruined eye, and it was he whom the buckskin-clad Barron approached. Tecumseh watched from the edge of the crowd.

Barron reached beneath his hunting shirt and removed a skin pouch, which he passed to Tenskwautawa. His weapons had been taken, but he kept a nervous hand on his powder horn, for there were ugly mutterings in the crowd. The Prophet unfolded the letter and scowled.

"What does this say, white man?"

"It says that Governor Harrison will gladly restore the Fort Wayne treaty lands—if you will first prove your ownership of them."

Back in the crowd, Tecumseh grimaced in disgust at the obvious contempt of the message. The Prophet also snorted in derision. He fingered the letter silently for a few moments. Then his face grew threatening.

"There have been other spies in Prophet's Town, white man," he said, "including one called Brouillette. Perhaps you shall not be as lucky as he." Tenskwautawa pointed one bony hand to the earth. "Perhaps this ground shall be your grave." The murmurs in the crowd grew more menacing, and Barron turned pale.

Tecumseh moved forward then, the crowd parting for him. He held out his hand to his brother. "Give the letter to me."

The Prophet obeyed without comment. Barron gave a weak, almost relieved smile. Tecumseh studied the writing on the paper, then handed it to Barron.

"You are not responsible for the insults of Harrison," Tecumseh said. "You have come with a duty, and in peace. Have no fear for your life."

Barron wiped the sweat from his upper lip. "Thank you."

"Please speak the words of the letter in Shawnee, for all to hear."

Barron did so. Its message was substantially what he had reported earlier, except that it contained an invitation for the Prophet to journey to Washington, the capital, to present his views on the ownership of the lands. Tecumseh's eyes narrowed in thought. Perhaps the time had come for the enemies to meet face to face, so that no last chance for peace might be overlooked.

"I am the one who speaks for the tribes," Tecumseh said with quiet authority. "Return to your leader and tell him the Prophet shall not go to Washington, but that Tecumseh shall go to Vincennes." His eyes darkened briefly. "I have many words to speak to the white governor who has stolen the land of our birthright."

11. PISTOLS AT GROUSELAND

On the morning of the eleventh of August, a small army of warriors moved down the sun-swept Wabash a few miles above Vincennes.

Proud and splendid in simple but elegant deerskin, a single eagle's feather thrust into his shining ebony hair, Tecumseh sat erect in the leading canoe. Though his face was composed, his eyes constantly darted to either shore. A long rifle rested against his moccasined foot in the bottom of the canoe, and the pair of braves manning the paddles were fully armed.

Directly behind, in another canoe, rode the Prophet, garbed in his most flamboyant robes, which were made of cloth and adorned with peculiar gold moons, triangles and other mystic shapes. And following the Prophet's craft came eighty more canoes and pirogues, each jammed with men. Harrison had sent directions that Tecumseh should limit his party to a small escort, but he had ignored the message. There were three hundred armed warriors with Tecumseh and his brother, and they were ready to fight if the occasion arose.

To the left Tecumseh sighted an open meadow behind a screen of sycamores. "We shall make our camp there and let the whites come to us," he said. "I have no doubt that spies have already ridden back to Vincennes with word of our arrival, and that a messenger will soon come riding out to us."

Within an hour the Indians, along with the squaws who had accompanied them, set up camp. They had no more than finished when a horseman approached along the river trail from the south. Tecumseh smiled grimly; his party had been seen, as he had suspected. The Prophet squinted with his one good eye. "It is the white man Barron."

Tecumseh rose. He raised his hand in the sign of friendship, which Barron returned from the opposite side of the meadow as he galloped toward the group of red men. Every voice in the meadow stilled. Heads turned, hands touched tomahawks. Barron rode forward and dismounted.

"Welcome, Shooting Star," the white man said, using the name which the Americans had given Tecumseh. "Governor Harrison sends his greetings. We received word of your coming from Captain Floyd, commander of Fort Knox."

Captain Floyd had sent a messenger ahead, warning Harrison that the Indians were coming in force. The message also stated that "they are headed by the brother of the Prophet—Tecumseh —who perhaps is one of the finest-looking men I ever saw . . . altogether a daring, bold-looking fellow."

After a few more preliminary remarks, Barron came to the heart of the matter. "The governor suggests tomorrow, Sunday, for the meeting. He wishes you to join him at his home."

"Return to Harrison and tell him that Tecumseh sets the time of the meeting," the Shawnee replied.

Barron was startled. "But why—?"

"My reasons are my own. Perhaps it shall be tomorrow, perhaps the following day. But I shall decide. That is my message to Harrison."

Reluctantly Barron mounted and rode south toward Vincennes. The Prophet shook his head in puzzlement, wishing to know why Tecumseh had delayed.

"Tenskwautawa, are you such a child that you fail to see what a perfect chance our coming presents to Harrison? Before I enter Vincennes, I want to be certain we shall come out again alive. No one knows what armies may wait in these woods, or what snares may be set. When I am satisfied that we are safe, only then will the meeting begin. Quickly, now. Call the scouts, have them search up and down the river."

There were a number of troops at Vincennes, but they seemed to be concentrated solely within the limits of the town. By the following Tuesday morning Tecumseh had satisfied himself as to the safety of his position. He felt that perhaps he had also gained a valuable advantage by making Harrison wait for him. Sending a runner ahead, and leaving the body of his force at the camp, Tecumseh, together with the Prophet and thirty warriors, set out on foot in the afternoon of the fourteenth of August for the fateful meeting.

Tecumseh walked at the head, the Prophet slightly behind. Then came the thirty men, scalp locks glistening, faces, arms and chests decorated in flaming scarlet. This guard was composed of the best warriors of the three hundred. Though they were clad in deerskin breeches and carried only tomahawks, Tecumseh walked confidently with them, sure of their fighting ability should there be trouble.

A troop of dragoons was quartered on the outskirts of the little city. The officers and men watched silently while the Indians marched by. Tecumseh glimpsed the small muskets, the pistols, the swords carried by the troops. Several men were polishing bayonets. A dead, frightening silence hung over Vincennes.

At the intersection of two dusty streets Joseph Barron waited on his horse. Silently he turned and led the procession between the cabins and shacks toward the imposing white building where Harrison made his headquarters. This was Grouseland, a tree-shaded place of elegant furnishings and simple dignity, a mansion fit for the tidewater of Virginia, built by the governor in the midst of his raw and muddy capital.

Barron led the way to the southwest side of the building. There near the veranda, a canopy had been erected above a shady arbor and chairs had been set out beneath on the cool lawn. Tecumseh drew up short.

Gathered at Grouseland were nearly all the important men of the Indiana Territory: justices of the court, merchants and military officers, as well as a sprinkling of white women watching discreetly from behind their fans at the rear of the group. Drawn up alongside the arbor, each with a massive dragoon pistol at his belt, were soldiers of a special honor guard platoon, under the command of a tough, red-jawed lieutenant.

Seated on one chair was Winimac, the Potawatomi chief who had helped Harrison with the Fort Wayne treaty. The obese, slovenly red man fearfully avoided Tecumseh's eye.

Seated across the arbor, two pistols on his hips, was John Gibson. Gibson was Secretary of the Indiana Territory, and Tecumseh had met him on occasion, for Gibson had lived with the Mingo and held the name Horsehead. Gibson's eyes crinkled not unpleasantly as he nodded in welcome.

And from the center chair, a sword at his side, tall, slim, erect, less than forty years old, a rather large-nosed man—sat the governor, William Henry Harrison.

"Welcome, Chief Tecumseh," Harrison said.

Barron, acting as interpreter, relayed the greetings back and forth. Tecumseh was introduced to all the notables present, including Colonel Francis Vigo, the swarthy Sardinian trader, who stepped briskly forward to shake the Shawnee's hand, a black cheroot tipped up from one corner of his mouth.

Tecumseh glanced warily at the arrangement of chairs beneath the canopy, and said, "This place is much like a house, which is for the white man's council. Men of the tribes council beneath the sky. It would please me to have the chairs for the whites taken into the open on the other side of the house. I sit upon the ground."

Frowning, Barron relayed this to Harrison. The answer came back: "Chief Tecumseh, your father desires that you should sit by his side."

Tecumseh raised one arm. "My only father is the Great Spirit. Tell Harrison we shall move into the open."

A rather annoyed look crossed the governor's face, but at last he complied with the request. The meeting site was removed from the arbor. Tecumseh took his place upon the ground while the other dignitaries arranged themselves, grumbling as they did so. Harrison said at last: "Shooting Star, you have come to Vincennes so that we might discuss the Fort Wayne lands. As my guest you enjoy the privilege of presenting your case. Please do so."

Tecumseh rose, handsome and majestic against the blue of the Indiana sky. He surveyed the circle of white faces. Of all times, his oratory must be superb now, if he were to change the governor's mind. With a final withering glance at the nervously fretting Winimac, who kept trying to hide his face behind the heads of other seated guests, and speaking softly but with passion, Tecumseh began his plea: "Brother, you have said that if we could show that the land of my people was sold by persons who had no right to sell, you would restore it. Those who did sell it did not own it. I speak for the owners—the Indians. The chiefs who sold it did so without our knowledge, but the tribes with *me* will not agree to it. If the land is not returned to us, when we go back to our homes you will soon see how it will be settled.

"The very notion of selling the sweet earth for white man's coin is false to begin with. Was not the land made for all our people by the Great Spirit? Was not the land created for those people who first dwelled upon it, the men of the tribes? If it is possible to place such land upon the auctioneer's platform, then perhaps the governor shall call another treaty conference in which he may purchase the air around us. And another at which he may buy the white clouds soaring overhead. Still another in which he may bargain to own every last drop of water which rolls in all the great lakes of our land!"

Harrison shifted uncomfortably in his chair, for Tecumseh's words were directed to him. The dragoons were restless. The red-jawed lieutenant kept exchanging significant looks with his men. Secretary John Gibson stroked one of the horse pistols strapped to his thigh. Winimac stared at the grass.

Tecumseh went on, his voice rising: "There is but one way in which we can stop this evil, and I have told it to you—that way is for the red men to unite in claiming a common and equal right in the land. That is how it was at first—and should be still—for the land was never divided but belongs to all, for the use of every one. No groups among us have a right to sell, even to one another, much less to strangers who want all and will not do with less."

Harrison winced under the brunt of Tecumseh's words, which mounted to a climax.

"If our land is not returned, we shall have a great council at which all the tribes will be present. Then we will show those who sold that they had no right to the claim they set up, and we will decide what shall be done with those chiefs. I am not alone in this. It is the determination of all the warriors and red people who follow me.

"Now listen to me well. If you do not rescind the treaty of Fort Wayne it will look as if you wished me to kill all the chiefs who sold you the land. I tell you I am authorized by the tribes to do this. I am the head of them all. I am a warrior, and all the warriors will meet together and then I will call those chiefs who sold you the land, and shall know what to do with them. If you do not restore the land, their blood shall be on your head."

Tecumseh's arm swept out, one finger pointing accusingly at Winimac. "And there sits one of the black dogs who presumed to speak for my people! He had no right! And should he doubt me, I will prove my words with a knife in his heart." Winimac shuddered and turned pale.

"I demand that all the lands of the Fort Wayne treaty be restored!" Tecumseh thundered. "I demand to hear, at this moment, from the governor's own lips, how quickly he plans to do what must be done!"

A sigh of appreciation, involuntarily given, escaped the lips of many spectators. Tecumseh sat down. Harrison toyed with the sword resting across his knees.

"I have a question to ask, Tecumseh," he said at length.

"Ask it, then."

"You are a member of which tribe?"

Tecumseh scowled. "The governor knows that I am a Shawnee."

"Certainly you will admit I speak the truth when I say that the Shawnee are a people not of the Indiana country, or even of the Ohio, but a people of the Georgia country to the south. The Shawnee came here even as my white brothers have done. Therefore I cannot reckon how you claim the lands for your own, when you were not an original owner either. Winimac, here, whom you reviled, truly has more right to speak than any man of the Shawnee."

Eyes blazing, Tecumseh retorted, "This is trickery with words! I have said that I speak not as a Shawnee, but as an Indian. I have said that I am a leader of many more tribes than one," he added, with a hint of threat in his voice.

The sharpness of Tecumseh's answer caused Harrison to meditate a few moments and begin his argument anew.

"Perhaps I may yet appeal to your reason, Chief Tecumseh,

for it is said that you are an educated man, and hearing you speak, I think it is so. Perhaps I may yet bring you to see the justice of the Fort Wayne treaty, when I point out that I believe the financial arrangements under which the land was purchased were eminently fair. A fair price was paid."

Harrison saw he had made a mistake, for Tecumseh was on his feet, shouting, "*The governor speaks a lie*!"

"The price was more than fair under the circumstances," Harrison persisted.

"*False*!" Tecumseh shouted. "*It is false*! *The governor lies*!"

Too late, Tecumseh felt his reason slipping away, overcome by the red heat of his anger. "*I have come to this town of Vincennes in good faith. . .*" he cried.

"Hold on!" John Gibson cried apprehensively, standing up.

"*. . . to be greeted with despicable lies from the tongue of a liar*," Tecumseh continued.

Harrison leaped erect, fist poised on his sword hilt.

"*Such lies shall bring nothing but bloodshed to you and all the whites*!" Tecumseh raged. His hand closed around his tomahawk. "*I am sickened by this council of liars with crooked tongues!*"

Harrison came forward a step, drawing his sword. "That will be enough!" he said in English. Gibson signaled to the dragoons and swiftly pistols and knives came free. Tecumseh's thirty braves had their tomahawks out with equal speed. One of the ladies on the fringe of the crowd shrieked. Tecumseh paced forward again. Harrison raised the point of his sword. The tough-jawed dragoon officer leveled his pistol at Tecumseh's head, resting it in the crook of his arm.

"This tin sword does not frighten me," Tecumseh said icily. "My braves are as many as the leaves that fall in autumn, and for such lies as you have given me, you shall soon feel the bite of *this*!"

He whipped up his tomahawk in a threatening arc. Then, in a space of seconds, his wrath cooled. He brought the weapon down and said, "All that you have said is false. You and the Seventeen Fires have cheated and imposed upon the Indians. You have never kept a treaty, and we have never broken one."

"The council is finished," Harrison replied coldly. "We cannot continue if you have no confidence in us."

"How can we have confidence in the white people?" Tecumseh demanded. "When Jesus Christ came upon the earth, you killed Him—and nailed Him to a cross. You thought He was dead, but you were mistaken. You have Shakers among you, and you laugh and make light of their worship. Everything I have said to you is the truth."

But Harrison was finished for the day. Without another word he climbed the veranda of Grouseland and disappeared indoors.

Bitter and ashamed, Tecumseh turned and led the Prophet and his men away. Gibson, Barron and the dragoons followed to the edge of the village. As Tecumseh marched toward his camp, he cursed his own hot temper. To lose control as he had done was the greatest humiliation, for he was a man, not an animal.

The following morning Barron called on Tecumseh in his camp. The Shawnee sent him back to Harrison with an apology, and requested that the talks be continued. The governor returned to the Indian camp with Barron.

When Harrison arrived, Tecumseh invited him to sit on a bench with him. They started talking, and as they talked the Indian moved so close to the governor that he was forced to move farther down the bench. Tecumseh continued doing this until Harrison was on the very edge of the bench and could move no farther. Finally, the American objected. But this was exactly what Tecumseh had expected.

"How would you enjoy being pushed all the way off?" he

asked. "That is the way the whites are treating my people—pushing them off their own lands. The Indians do not enjoy it either. They object, but their objections mean nothing."

Tecumseh and Harrison continued talking for several hours, but it was apparent that they could never agree. Tecumseh made up his mind quickly. He had presented the Americans with the opportunity for peace and had received only falsehoods. He would go to the British at once.

12. "I CANNOT STRAY FROM MY PATH . . ."

A cool autumn wind blew from the northwest that fifteenth of November in 1810, stripping away the last leaves from the trees that shimmered on Bois Blanc Island in the mouth of the Detroit River. Marching at Tecumseh's side was the ramrod-stiff Major Taylor of His Majesty's Hundredth Regiment of the British Line. Other officers and men of the regiment were drawn up on the parade ground here at Fort Malden, Canada—the British outpost at the northern edge of the village of Amherstburg, just across the Detroit from the American shore. Major Taylor led Tecumseh to the place from which he would be allowed to speak to the British.

This was Tecumseh's first visit among the troops of George III, the Great King, and he was filled with awe. They appeared very tough and hard and proper in their blazing scarlet coats and white breeches.

Major Taylor stepped back a pace. He relayed his message to an interpreter: "You may proceed, Chief Tecumseh." He said it rather snappishly, in a clipped accent. Tecumseh had a premonition that the British did not wholly welcome his presence. Foreign matters still occupied their thoughts. Nevertheless, he spoke firmly: "To my very good friends in the army of the Great King, I bring greetings from my people below the lake."

His oration was brief yet powerful. He sketched the plan of

the alliance of the tribes, concluding with an urgent plea for arms and supplies in the event of war. Taylor dismissed the troops when he finished, and Tecumseh accompanied a party of officers back to the fort for a talk.

"As I pointed out earlier," Major Taylor said, "we are in a delicate position, since we are not at this time actively engaged in warfare with the Americans. At the same time, however, we are short on provisions for our own people. This little dot on the map—Amherstburg—is not quite the most important place in the Empire, you know. Our pleas fall on deaf ears in Whitehall, granted they ever reach that far."

"Still," said Ensign Dawson, a Britisher who had worked with the Department of Indian Affairs, "our guest is a leader amongst his people, and it's no flattery to say it. You know as clearly as I, Major Taylor, there's a storm of trouble brewing. Personally, I'll look the chief straight in the face and cast my vote for doing everything possible to have him with us."

Captain Gore said dryly, "Hear! Hear!"

After some additional discussion, Tecumseh at last won a grudging verdict from Major Taylor. Taking his leave swiftly, after offering proper thanks, the Shawnee returned to his camp at the edge of Amherstburg, where Shabbona waited eagerly.

"What news?"

"I have received promises from Taylor that our people who remain loyal to the Great King shall be provisioned to the limit of the ability of the British here. True, the outpost is not well off." Tecumseh clapped Shabbona on the shoulder, managing a smile. "Yet it is a point won. From Harrison we got lies and insults, while from the British we win promises of help. If there are those of our people harassed by the Long Knives, they may come to Malden for refuge and shelter. In this way I can take care of their wants and protect them."

"And should the fighting come—what then?"

"Taylor was impatient. We talked little of war, but—" Tecumseh's smile widened again, almost slyly. "They spoke words of praise about me, Shabbona. I am not one for boasting. I tell you only because I believe they will accept my knife when I offer it. Quickly, now! Gather the warriors. We must cross the river and return to Prophet's Town."

On the return trip they spread the news of the hospitality of the Great King's officers at Malden. All across the northern frontier the word traveled, and the trickle of red immigrants into Fort Malden became a widening stream as the new year opened. Those too old, too young or too frail to remain in the forest and fight journeyed north, crossed the river to Canada and made their homes around Amherstburg. There they received grudging but regular issues of blankets and copper kettles as well as tobacco, flints, powder and shot. And when these supplies ran low, there were such odd commodities as garishly patterned cotton cloth or carving knives or small hand mirrors or combs. News of this caused Tecumseh to smile tolerantly. Though the British were not completely happy about the situation, at least they kept their word.

The year 1811 set the frontier whispering of danger and evil, for omens and strange symbols were everywhere. The skies opened day after day, and great rains poured endlessly from swollen, malevolent clouds. A comet streaked burning in the heavens in the month of March, and the spring squirrels plunged through the forests in great armies, madly, without direction, as though fleeing something ominous. And at last, early in July, Captain Walter Wilson, a rather burly, unpleasant American officer, journeyed the river to Prophet's Town with a message. He confronted Tecumseh and the Prophet by the latter's throne chair, with a large crowd assembled.

"Has Tecumseh heard of the Potawatomi who have killed the

whites at the Randolph homestead in the Illinois lands?" Wilson demanded.

"I have heard," Tecumseh said. "Such brutality does not please me. I believe in fighting when necessary, but I do not believe in butchery."

"Oh, I'm sure of that," Wilson said, obviously meaning just the opposite. "And of course the mighty Shooting Star has no idea where the fugitive murderers are hiding."

Tecumseh's mouth made a tight line. "They are not here, if that is what you wish to know." Actually he had heard that the fugitives were hiding with the Potawatomi chief Main Poe near the village of Peoria, but his face did not betray the knowledge. Wilson snorted, his contempt deepening.

"Governor Harrison demands you surrender these killers."

"I have said they are not here."

"Harrison *demands* their surrender!"

"White man," Tecumseh cried furiously, "your words strike me in the face and brand me a teller of lies! I do not harbor the men you seek. If I did, I would not turn them over to you or the governor."

"That's treasonous talk," Wilson threatened.

"Should a red man kill a white, the justice is swift. But when one of your race slays one of mine, that is sport. There is no punishment. This you cannot deny, white man, because I have ears and eyes. Your words insult my ears. Return to Harrison and tell him that I shall be with him not many days from now. At that time we can speak of murder and murderers, of justice and of Fort Wayne."

"The white man's tongue is evil!" cried a voice out of the crowd assembled around the Prophet's throne chair.

Another voice shouted, "Give him a taste of Long Knife justice—a spear in his entrails!"

Furiously Tecumseh swung on the crowd. "Have you not

heard my very words? Are you such animals that you cannot comprehend what I have said but a moment before? Let there be silence. Take the white man to the river and do not harm him; for if you do, the man who harms him shall answer to me. Now go."

Wilson, cursing and threatening, was seized and hurried out of the village by members of the silenced crowd, to carry back the news of Tecumseh's second journey to Vincennes.

One final attempt, Tecumseh had spoken to himself in the quiet of his own mind. *One last time to try to open the eyes of the governor.*

Though he felt it was practically hopeless, he despised the thought of war, and was willing to humble himself once more by approaching Harrison with a plea for fairness and redress of wrongs.

Eighteen days later, in the moist, fiery heat of the Wabash bottoms, Tecumseh, the Prophet, Shabbona, Billy Caldwell and three hundred members of various tribes again moved down the Wabash. But Captain Wilson, in company with several other white scouts, was waiting to halt their progress at the tiny way station of Bosseron, about twenty miles above Vincennes.

"Your party is too large," Wilson said. "You cannot come to Vincennes with more than two dozen."

Shabbona tugged Tecumseh's arm. "A trap. . ."

While Tecumseh pondered, Wilson shrugged indifferently. "Very well. You meet the governor on his terms this time, or not at all."

"The terms of the governor are insulting," Billy Caldwell said sourly.

"But we will accept," Tecumseh said at last. "The wrong must not be on our side. We must not be so haughty that we forget our purpose."

The meeting on the cool porch at Grouseland was short and

unfriendly. After the last conference, Harrison clearly had little patience with Tecumseh. Tecumseh had firmly set his mind on keeping an even temper, but the moment he entered a plea for reconsideration of the Fort Wayne treaty dealings, Harrison shook his head.

"I am not in a position to conduct negotiations concerning my recent purchases," he said curtly. "I will enter no such negotiations. The only person with power to conduct such a discussion is Mr. Madison, our president. If the chief Tecumseh wishes to journey overland to the city of Washington, he is most welcome to do so. But that is my only answer."

"Does the governor act in good faith?" Tecumseh inquired coolly.

"Good faith!" Harrison snorted. "Good faith indeed! If you want to speak of good faith, you should first hand over to me those renegade Potawatomi who slaughtered the homesteaders so brutally in Illinois."

"I told your emissary Wilson that I was not hiding the Potawatomi."

Harrison said nothing for a moment. "Another act of good faith would be the immediate cancellation of your trip to the southern states," he suggested. Tecumseh's face grew startled as Harrison went on. "Oh, yes, I am informed of your plans. It is well known that you are going to travel among the southern tribes again, to unite them for some unknown purpose." The final words clearly indicated that Harrison was afraid the purpose could be nothing short of war.

"Our confederation," Tecumseh said carefully, "shall first be a peaceful one. We did not chastise you when the Thirteen Fires joined to resist the Great King."

"That was many years ago," Harrison replied shortly. "The situation has changed. I can only say that I regard this trip as an unfriendly act."

Reluctantly Tecumseh said, "I cannot stray from my path. So be it."

Harrison shot a suspicious glance at Tecumseh. Was he planning the first step in an uprising which would lead to wholesale war? Though he could not be absolutely certain, Harrison believed this was true.

Defeated once again, Tecumseh left Vincennes with nothing accomplished and a wider gulf between Harrison and his people. Putting this unhappy state of affairs from his mind, he rejoined his followers near Bosseron. He called Shabbona and the Prophet to his side and issued orders:

"Take the people again up the Wabash to Prophet's Town. The time is here for the southern journey. I will take twenty-four men with me."

After the Prophet had moved off, Shabbona spoke intently: "I wish my brother Tecumseh would let me be his companion."

"I have need of you by Tenskwautawa's side. Though he is my blood, I sometimes believe his own notions have damaged his mind. Should there be danger, he is not fit to guide our people. I will have good counsel with my friend Jim Blue Jacket at my side, and Seekaboo, the Creek, can speak many tongues. I put into your hands the leadership at Prophet's Town, Shabbona. For this task I would choose only the man I trust most."

Shabbona nodded silently.

Twenty-five warriors started south along the Wabash on the fifth of August, 1811, to gather the combined strength of all the southern tribes before the nearing storm of war crashed around their heads.

This silent, deadly and splendid force of two dozen men and a single leader might have been cut from one mold. They were painted alike, armed and dressed alike, with buckskin leggings and shirts, with fringed moccasins, with rifles, scalp knives, tomahawks, war clubs, with hair shaved off—all but a glistening scalp lock which hung at the shoulder in three braids. But there was one difference. The honor guard of twenty-four wore hawk feathers in their heads, held in place by thin silver bands. Tecumseh wore only two crane feathers. A white one, which meant he came in peace; and a red one, which meant war with Harrison and the whites.

They moved down the sprawling Mississippi to the Chickasaw Bluffs. There, the great trail began—a trail upon which Tecumseh poured out his soul, pleading for the salvation of all the tribes through unity.

The trail ran from the Chickasaw Bluffs along the torturous hundred-and-sixty-mile road to the Chickasaw villages in Tennessee. . . to the Chickasaw farmers who had given up war and hunting to plant pumpkins and pecans, wild fruit and hickory nuts. . . to the lodge of the sachem Colbert who refused to join Tecumseh, for the Chickasaw were then at peace.

The trail ran out, cutting southeast, down to the Choctaw with the flattened heads. . . to the delta of the wild Yazoo. . . to the Six Towns Trail of the Mississippi. . . to the house of the great chief Pushmataha at Hoentubbee's Town, where Tecumseh's oratory rose to an impassioned pitch.

"Where today are the Pequot," he cried dramatically to the Choctaw. "Where are the Narraganset, the Mohican, the Pocanoket and many other once powerful tribes of our people? They have vanished before the greed and oppression of the white man, as snow before a summer sun. In the vain hope of defending alone their ancient possessions, they have fallen in the wars. Look over their once beautiful country, and what do you see now? Nothing but the ravages of the white man. So it will be with the Choctaw and Chickasaw! Soon your mighty forest trees will be cut down to fence in the land which the white intruders dare call their own! Soon their broad roads will pass over the graves of your fathers and the places of their rest will be blotted out forever!"

But the Choctaw had sworn to be the friends of the Long Knives, and they could not be swayed, not even by Tecumseh. They did not wish to fight.

So the trail knifed on into the water oak country, across the Tombigbee River into Alabama on crude rafts lashed with grapevine. . . out of the tulip tree and honeysuckle country deep into the canebrakes of the Creek nation. . . to Tuckabatche and Muskoogee Town along the Tallapoosa, the town of Tecumseh's mother.

"Let the white race perish!" Tecumseh exclaimed to the Creek. "They seize your land, they corrupt your women, they trample on the grass of your dead. They must be driven back upon a trail of blood. . . back into the great waters that brought them to our shores! Burn their houses, destroy their cattle. The red man owns the country and the white man must never enjoy it. This is the will of the Great Spirit!"

The warriors of the Creek nation greeted Tecumseh's plan with enthusiasm, but Big Warrior, their chief, did not approve. He called Tecumseh a "bad man" who was trying to start a war in which many Indians would be killed, and he would have nothing to do with the confederation.

"Your blood is white!" Tecumseh cried angrily. "You have taken my talk and the wampum and the hatchet, but you do not mean to fight. I know the reason. You do not believe that the Great Spirit has sent me. You shall know that it is so! When I return to Tippecanoe, I shall stamp my foot on the ground and shake down every house in Tuckabatche!"

This was certainly a wild threat, but it frightened the Creek tribe. They often talked over this promise of destruction and carefully estimated the number of days Tecumseh would require to return to Tippecanoe. When the final day arrived, a terrible rumbling was heard, and suddenly many of the tepees and lodges toppled over. The Creek were terrified. "Tecumseh has arrived at the Tippecanoe!" they cried in alarm. "His threat has come true! We must join his nation or die!"

But Tecumseh had had nothing to do with the rumblings in Tuckabatche. It is doubtful that he even knew they occurred. However, the New York *Herald* of the twenty-sixth of February reported: "The Indians say the Shawnee Prophet has caused the earthquake to destroy the whites."

After leaving the Creek, the Shawnee and his little party plunged through Georgia, where the Seminole refused to join the Indian confederation. Then they swept north up the Chattahoochee River, toward the smoldering mist of the Blue Ridge Mountains. . . across the Soco Gap to the chiefs of the eastern Cherokee. . . to Junaluska, the sachem who wanted no war for the Cherokee.

Then the trail swept out through the perilous land along the slopes of the mountains of the Ozark, where Tecumseh spoke to the savage Osage. But despite his oratory, the Osage refused. They wanted nothing to do with Tecumseh and his plan. They would fight if attacked, but they would fight alone.

Then the trail moved north again, across the Smoky Mountains through Tennessee to the Illinois country. A sad trail, a trail of sorrow, of bitterness, of frustration. A trail of more than a thousand miles and a mighty dream, turning eastward again at last, up to the frozen Wabash in the gray-white winter desolation of February, 1812. . . up the Tippecanoe.

And then the trail stopped on a frozen, bone-cold morning. Fingers and toes were numb, breath ghosted in the air. . . and the mind of Tecumseh cried out in fear of madness.

Was this Old Piqua again? No word had reached him through the wintry forest wastelands, but he thought, horrifyingly, that it must be Piqua all over again.

The cabins and wigwams were in ruins, the land burned black, the fields gutted. And through it all moved listless, beaten figures, his own defeated people.

He saw it clearly in the gray February light, from where he sat his pony on a little clearing along the Tippecanoe, his twenty-four weary braves just behind, murmuring among themselves.

It was not madness. It was Prophet's Town—burned, looted, destroyed while he had been riding the southern trail.

The horror of the sight swelled in his mind until finally, with a strangled shriek of pain, Tecumseh hurled his pony forward, down through the snow toward the desolation.

13. THE RED TOMAHAWK RISES

That evening a thin, whistling wind cut around the corners of the meetinghouse in which the leaders gathered—Billy Caldwell, the Prophet, Shabbona, Jim Blue Jacket and Tecumseh. Tecumseh had spent the day inspecting the damage in his burned Tippecanoe town. A few hovels and wigwams had been restored, a small game supply had been raised, but even this effort had taken its toll—that was clear from the gaunt, worry-ravaged face of Shabbona. The Prophet, on the other hand, appeared untroubled. He peered at his hands with dreamy preoccupation.

Shabbona spat away a scrap of deer meat. "I have no stomach for eating when our people starve out there in the night wind."

"I have already sent the young warriors into the woods, every one of them," Tecumseh said, "for my people must be cared for above all else. My share of food has been given to the children," he went on, "and I tell you this not to paint myself a hero, but to show you the sort of example we must set if we are to teach our people the way of true men."

Shabbona put aside the rest of the deer meat, shamefaced.

"Now," Tecumseh said, "before this council ends I wish to hear the story of the battle. You have told me that the man who burned our town was Harrison."

Shabbona's mouth hardened. "That is right."

"I left you in command of the people, Shabbona," Tecumseh chided gently.

Shabbona jerked up his head. He glared at the Prophet. Then he spoke: "While you made this clear to me, I fear it was not made as clear to your brother, for the people listened to him. When I tell my story, you may think I speak with a split tongue, because I will speak against the Prophet. But every word which fills my tale is an honest word."

Tecumseh glanced at his brother. "He does not even speak out in his own favor."

"He has behaved strangely since the battle," Shabbona replied.

"Tell me of the battle, before I make my judgment on him. I have already made my judgment on Harrison, for he struck a coward's blow when he attacked. Prophet's Town does not lie within the treaty lands which Harrison claims he purchased! It is our land, and well he knows it. When he marched upon us, he challenged us to war!"

"Undoubtedly he was afraid of our growing power," Billy Caldwell said. "He showed his fear plainly at Vincennes, when he asked that the southern trip be abandoned."

Tecumseh nodded. The wind keened down the Tippecanoe, thin and bitter and mocking, crying sadly of defeat, of homelessness and starvation, of white treachery. Tecumseh's voice was a whisper, but his eyes glittered. "The battle. . ."

The preceding September, Shabbona related, Governor Harrison assembled a force of one thousand soldiers at Vincennes. He marched forth along the left—or northernmost—bank of the Wabash River. Spies carried a report of the invaders to the Prophet, who hastily organized a delegation to make peace. This group crossed the Tippecanoe and proceeded down the right—or southern—riverbank. The Prophet had not more than four hundred warriors gathered in the village.

"Why did you march down the wrong bank of the river?" Tecumseh raged.

The Prophet lifted his single eye, smiled in a distant way and replied in a tone of gentle reproof. "I was not certain of the location of the army of the whites. I planned to counsel with them, and if they would remain on the opposite side of the river, there would be no struggle. I believed I could prevent them from crossing."

"Shabbona was to lead the braves in the event of a battle!" Tecumseh said sharply. "But I did not wish a battle now! Our force is not strong enough."

"I was not aware of Shabbona's leadership," the Prophet said coldly.

So the warriors from Prophet's Town had been cleverly foxed by Governor Harrison, who camped to the west of the village. There was a time of fruitless peace talk. Then, according to Shabbona, a core of war-eager Winnebago within the village had demanded that the braves attack. The attack was repulsed, the defendants of Prophet's Town defeated and scalps were taken by Harrison's men—scalps that were divided into sections so that each soldier in the white army could claim a prize of victory. Then the village was burned and looted while the inhabitants fled into the forest, many of them toward Fort Malden. And Harrison, triumphant, had ridden back down the Wabash toward his capital.

"You ordered the attack?" Tecumseh asked his brother.

Tenskwautawa gave an indifferent shrug. "I have grown weary of thinking about the battle."

Tecumseh leaped to his feet, a single vein in his left temple beating furiously. "Think of it when I command you to think of it! You were not supposed to attack the whites unless you were first attacked!"

"My brother Tecumseh was many hundreds of miles distant.

The Winnebago were all around, very angry, knives in their hands. I chanted prayers for them as they fought. It was what they would have me do. There was no choice." Again the Prophet shrugged. "It is of no matter."

"No matter that our forces have been cut to pieces and scattered? That our central gathering place has been destroyed? You have slashed off my arm, my brother. The times are too perilous for me to allow you further control. At dawn tomorrow," Tecumseh said quietly, "gather no more than a dozen followers to guard your person, and leave this village. You have shown yourself weak and incapable of directing our people."

Tecumseh's wrathful order did not seem to disturb the Prophet. "I have no heart for the cause," the Prophet said laconically. "Lately I have had less and less opportunity to commune with the spirits who tell me of holy things. I must regain the true way, Tecumseh. I have left the trail of the righteous these past months. I am glad to be sent away, because you lead our people into war."

With a kind of pitiful majesty about his tattered robes, the Prophet rose and strode slowly to the council house entrance. There he turned. Gusts of snow blew about his head, giving him a weird, wind-whipped halo of glistening white crystals. In an eerie, crackling voice he said:

"I leave this council fire willingly, because in the heart of the flame I have seen death, and all who sit around it shall die when the evil war begins."

So at dawn, with half a dozen men, three women and two small children in his retinue, the Prophet rode out from the Tippecanoe village chanting a white man's hymn, riding into the frosty wasteland to the west, head thrown back, a strange and demented leader vanishing for the last time from the eyes of his older brother.

Standing alone and chilled in the dawn, Tecumseh watched

the caravan ride out. His heart felt touched with sadness. Then he realized Shabbona was standing at his elbow. The younger man spoke:

"I know how my brother Tecumseh feels, for he is your flesh."

"He could do us nothing but harm," Tecumseh said, though doubtfully. "Perhaps my heart has grown hard, but I have long since put away my own feelings. If our people are to be saved when the battle comes there must be no mistakes."

Shabbona deemed it prudent to say nothing more. Tecumseh lowered his head. He walked alone a pace or two, staring emptily into the bleak and burnt forest along the river's shore. Also in the winter, many years ago, there had been another leave-taking. *Rebecca. . .*

And then it was green, bursting spring along the Tippecanoe. The fuse of war had burned down short. Tecumseh dwelled alone—and lonely—in a small hut amidst the ruins. Watching, waiting.

Every day spies raced into Prophet's Town. From Ohio to the Illinois lands scattered fires were breaking out—the red tomahawks of war were being raised.

In April the Potawatomi took the warpath against the whites. Scalps hung drying in the sun in Illinois. Homesteads were burned. The nights rang with the cries of dying white men. Tecumseh's men had no part in these actions, yet the killings clearly showed the Shawnee leader that the war was breaking.

Along the frontier roads and creeks the settlers moved to the forts in a panic-stricken flight for protection. Blockhouse ports began to bristle with long rifles. The ring of hammers building still other forts echoed in the Indiana country. And in scattered places, more and more frequently, the red tomahawk came chopping down.

Five miles outside of Harrison's own Vincennes a white family died.

Bands of settlers were ambushed just outside the walls of Fort Dearborn, at the foot of Lake Michigan.

Long Knife armies were moving through the woods. Soldiers of the Great King poured into Fort Malden.

April with its beauty became April with its dark drum roll of approaching war.

Tecumseh had managed to regroup his forces along the Tippecanoe. He gathered nearly six hundred warriors, from twelve tribes. Torches burned all night long. Every pair of hands capable of work fashioned weapons. Against the background of frantic activity in the village sounded sharp cries of alarm as spies raced in to report the actions of the enemy.

Would the combined tribes be able to withstand the power of the Americans—and would the British aid them? These questions, Tecumseh knew, would soon be answered in the clang of battle.

Signs that the conflict was coming at almost any hour were reinforced when Harrison retired from Vincennes on the orders of President James Madison. Return Jonathan Meigs, the governor of Ohio, replaced Harrison, who moved into the field to prepare for an important role in the forthcoming military campaign. On the sixth of April, 1812, Meigs called for troops at the junctions of the Miami and Mad Rivers at the town of Dayton. These twelve hundreds soldiers of the Ohio army, commanded by Brigadier General William Hull, moved north from Dayton on the first of June by order of President Madison. Tecumseh realized clearly that Hull marched for no other purpose but to fight.

On the eighteenth day of June, 1812, the American Congress completed adoption of the resolution which opened the war against Great Britain—the war through which the Americans were determined to remove for all time the soldiers of George III from the North American continent. With the fur-rich northwest country as the prize, and with the British Orders in Council closing the ports of Europe to American shipping as the goal, the war exploded in full fury across the frontier.

The messenger who came to the Tippecanoe town was Isadore, the Wyandot chief.

"Chief Tecumseh," he said, "the red tomahawks have been lifted against the British king by Madison, President of the Seventeen Fires."

"Then it is here at last," Tecumseh breathed.

"General Hull has reached Fort Wayne, and has asked that Tecumseh come there to sit in council."

Tecumseh knew clearly the meaning of this—the crisis, the turning point. The Long Knives awaited his final decision. "Return and tell General Hull that I will march to Fort Wayne to tell him what I think of his war."

In a great and splendidly decorated wigwam on the parade ground at Fort Wayne, Tecumseh and Isadore sat before General Hull. Beyond the fort waited two hundred of Tecumseh's warriors, as well as scattered elements from many of the tribes, for there was no man on the whole frontier who did not want to hear Tecumseh's declaration.

Isadore, acting as interpreter, presented Hull's request:

"The President of the Seventeen Fires says that he values the friendship of Tecumseh. He asks that Tecumseh give his word that the tribes who owe him allegiance will take no part in the war. In return for this, there will be friendship given and protection of all red brothers."

While Hull watched, half suspicious, half eager, Isadore stepped forward bearing the pipe of peace.

"How can there be protection for my people?" Tecumseh questioned. "If the Long Knives must fight the Great King, when will they find a single moment of a single day to protect the tribes? The Great King is powerful. He will not pause in his battle so that General Hull may protect my people."

When Isadore relayed this message, Hull scowled apprehensively. Tecumseh went on: "Will the treaty lands be restored to their rightful owners?"

"This I cannot promise," Hull replied. Tecumseh drew himself up, reached forward and took the pipe of peace. Hull glanced at Isadore in surprise.

Then, sharply, Tecumseh broke the pipe in half and threw it to the ground.

Isadore asked quickly, "Does this mean that Chief Tecumseh has made up his mind to lift the red tomahawk against the Seventeen Fires?"

"I will decide in good time," Tecumseh replied. "The parlay is ended." And he turned and stalked from the wigwam.

That night, his decision made, Tecumseh and his warriors sped north through the wilderness. There were Shawnee, Kickapoo, Potawatomi and Delaware. . . a tough fighting force traveling swiftly across the frontier. The war had come. Tecumseh was determined to waste no time in joining the British at Fort Malden.

14. THE IRON SOLDIER SPEAKS

In July Tecumseh and his forest army crossed to Bois Blanc Island and then to Fort Malden. The British garrison, temporarily commanded by Colonel Thomas St. George, feverishly prepared for war as runners and spies brought news of Hull's sweeping march to Fort Detroit.

Tecumseh welcomed the bands of braves pouring into the fort—savage Sauk and Fox, roving parties of bloodthirsty Wyandot, Potawatomi led by the sachem Main Poe. The red men soon numbered close to a thousand, and this force was strengthened by the three hundred British troops at the fort, tough fighting veterans of the Forty-first Line Regiment and the Newfoundland Fencibles.

The American army moved up the west shore of the river, past Malden, to Fort Detroit. Hull arrived at the American post on the night of the fifth of July. On the twelfth, with three thousand men, heavy cannon and lightning-fast cavalry, he crossed the river to the town of Sandwich and mounted the invasion of Canada. Spies brought a fearsome proclamation—if Tecumseh's people joined the British, Hull would show no mercy. He would spread death and desolation if the red men took a single white scalp.

Meanwhile, Tecumseh moved north to the Aux Canards River, four miles above Malden, and there, with a small force of warriors and men of the Amherstburg militia, he fought the first battle of the War of 1812.

A bridge spanned the marshes of the river, and the American army had to cross this bridge. Tecumseh's forces defended it until two hundred Yankees, commanded by Colonel Lewis Cass, forded the river at another point, crept up from behind and drove Tecumseh into retreat.

July dragged on. Hull camped at Sandwich and did not advance, though the wooden construction of Fort Malden, coupled with the intense dry heat, made the garrison a tinderbox which could easily have been destroyed by artillery. While the British pondered the riddle of Hull's sudden cowardice and indecision, Tecumseh and several hundred warriors crossed the river to the American side, under the shadowy guns of the four hundred-ton British warship *Queen Charlotte,* anchored threateningly up the river.

Tecumseh's purpose was to attack and destroy Hull's lines of communication from the south. At the Raisin River, thirty-five miles below Detroit, a convoy of two hundred Americans with fresh provisions waited for a safe escort by Hull's troops north to Detroit. Tecumseh planned swiftly and shrewdly. He deployed his men on the road the convoy would take to pass through Brownstown, on the Huron River. From the north, Major Thomas Van Horne with a force of men swooped down to rescue the supply caravan.

On the fourth of August, on a dusty road between a tree-shaded creek and a cornfield just outside Brownstown, Tecumseh struck Van Horne from ambush.

When the convoy passed that way, they saw long poles planted by the roadside, each with a grim warning hanging from its tip, fluttering in the breeze—a white scalp. Like a woods ghost, Tecumseh had gone. But his victory was mixed with despair, for he had tried vainly to stop the scalping of the dead, yet even his powerful, respected voice had been unable to calm the passion for revenge which his warriors felt.

At Brownstown he had captured dispatches going south from Detroit. These he returned to the British officers at Malden. The messages, from various junior officers serving with Hull, complained bitterly of the commander's cowardice and his indecision. Should he attack Malden? Did the red men outnumber his force too greatly? The British officers, with danger and death lurking close, prayed that Hull would not suddenly grow bold.

Then there was fresh news—a report that Michilimackinac Island, in Lake Michigan, had fallen to the British. In a cloud of dust, General Hull moved his army back across the river to Fort Detroit, fearing an attack from the rear.

Again an American force was assembled, this time six hundred troops, to rescue the convoy crawling northward from the Raisin River. With two hundred and fifty warriors and British troops, Tecumseh and Major Adam Muir crossed the river to Monguaga, between Brownstown and Detroit, to meet the rescue force. Arriving roughly six hours ahead of the rescue army, they set the ambush in a low valley thick with oak trees. At three o'clock on Sunday, the ninth of August, the vanguard of the American force entered the valley.

For a time it seemed that the outnumbered red men would carry the fight. Then, abruptly, a rifle ball caught Tecumseh in the leg. Without his voice to cry orders, Major Muir became confused and the British line crumbled. As Tecumseh lay out of sight, frantically pressing black earth into his wound to stem the flow of blood, the leaderless braves broke and retreated.

Through the night the defeated army straggled back across the river. Tecumseh himself, sweat stained, dirty and weak from loss of blood, received a grim shock when he and Muir reported to the commander of the garrison—and found not Colonel St. George, but Colonel Henry A. Procter.

Procter was a round-faced Briton with bland eyes and a small, curling mouth. He was foppishly dressed in gleaming red and white when all his men were begrimed from days of battle. He dusted his nostrils with a handkerchief as he sat behind his desk in the fort and listened to the report of the Monguaga defeat.

Tecumseh disliked the man instantly, feeling that he was no soldier and knew nothing of fighting—that he was not to be trusted.

"It was to be expected, Muir," Procter said in a broad tone. "I don't feel that these red savages can be of much assistance in civilized warfare."

Tecumseh stiffened, angered. Muir came to his defense:

"Without Chief Tecumseh, Colonel Procter, I fear Fort Malden would be in Hull's hands by this time."

"Oh, I doubt that, Major. I quite doubt that. In any event, I have taken command, and I am fully capable of holding Fort Malden—and using only regular troops to do so." With a disdainful eye on Tecumseh he added, "You may go. Major Muir will present the remainder of the report."

Furious at the rebuff, Tecumseh returned to his camp at the edge of the fort. Shabbona listened to the news with anger. "I have seen this Procter. He is a toad, a cowering little child in the stuffed body of a man."

"He is the commander," Tecumseh finished bitterly. "We must obey him, or lose the friendship of the Great King."

For days this intolerable situation continued. Troops were dispatched upon regular missions, but not once did Colonel Procter indicate that he recognized the presence of the vast force of red fighting men at Malden. Then stirring talk whispered through the fort. Procter was to be relieved of command because there was to be a new arrival—Isaac Brock, lieutenant governor of Canada. Toward midnight some days later Billy Caldwell trotted into Tecumseh's camp.

"I have seen this Brock! He is a giant, a man of yellow hair and big arms like iron. He has called for a meeting of all officers of the fort, to be held in less than an hour's time."

Decisively Tecumseh arose. Stepping impatiently outside, he called, "I am sick of Procter's bitter tongue. I will meet this Brock and see if he is a better man. Come, Shabbona."

Tecumseh marched to the fort and demanded to be taken to Brock.

"There is an important meeting. . ." the guard began.

In English Tecumseh shot back: "I am the leader of the Shawnee. Take me to Brock."

The guard lowered his eyes meekly. "This way."

Resolutely Tecumseh and Shabbona followed the sentry across the compound to the officers' barracks. The two men waited in the mist-laden night air while the sentries whispered to one another; then Colonel Matthew Elliot, the even-tempered British Indian Agent for the Canadian Territory, appeared. Elliot listened to Tecumseh's request for an audience with Brock, then shook his head rather doubtfully.

"Major General Brock is quite busy with the officers of the fort, and. . ."

"Is this Brock taking command? Shall I be serving under him?"

"Why, yes, that's a fact, but—"

"Then take me in to him, for I have a right to speak with the man who commands the loyalty of my people."

Unable to resist the firmness of Tecumseh's glance and tone, Elliot reluctantly led the way into the headquarters room. All talk ceased immediately. Heads turned. Colonel Procter gasped.

"*Really*, Elliot—!"

Beneath the low, rough hewn ceiling of the room, clouds of pipe smoke floated. Tecumseh's eyes swept the group, picking out the one person he did not know. His mouth relaxed instantly.

He was pleased by what he saw. From behind a scrolled writing desk, Major General Isaac Brock rose as Colonel Elliot stepped forward.

"Please excuse the interruption, General Brock. This is Chief Tecumseh, the Shawnee who fights with us. He was extremely anxious to be presented, sir."

"Welcome, Shooting Star," Brock rumbled in his rich, warm voice. He stepped around the desk, a brawny, six-foot-three Britisher from the Isle of Guernsey.

Brock's steel-blue eyes appraised Tecumseh quickly. The Shawnee extended his own hand, and his strength was met by that of Brock. Without question and without reservation Tecumseh—in an instant—placed his full confidence in this strapping soldier in the brilliant scarlet coat and white breeches. Their handclasp was one of sudden and genuine friendship, for Brock was equally impressed with the regal figure in his elegant deerskins. Tecumseh turned his head slightly and said to Shabbona:

"At last a *man* commands Fort Malden."

Brock smiled tolerantly. Colonel Procter rose hastily to protest.

"Really, General Brock, I must strongly recommend adjournment of this most important meeting until your courtesies"—the words of Procter dripped contempt—"to this red Indian are concluded."

"For heaven's sake, Procter!" the general exclaimed sharply. "I've been tossing and heaving on that blasted lake five days and nights. I'm half starved; I'm sick to death for want of sleep—and on top of it I must endure your petty concern for niceties of conduct which are hardly binding on this Godforsaken frontier. We are fighting a war, my dear colonel, not viewing a polite entertainment at Covent Garden! May I remind you that I am quite aware of the splendid fighting record of Chief Tecumseh in the short time he has been at Malden? It was he who led the fighting at Brownstown, I'm told, and who returned the captured dispatches from Detroit. He also bolstered Major Muir's attack at Monguaga."

While Colonel Procter fidgeted in embarrassed discomfort, Isaac Brock thumped one massive fist on the writing table.

"If I were to include in this meeting only those persons who have thus far distinguished themselves in battle, Procter, I fear I should invite Chief Tecumseh to remain, while requesting you to leave."

Procter sank into humiliated silence. Brock gestured toward a chair near the desk. "Please be seated, Chief Tecumseh. Your companion will find a vacant place there by the hearth." When Tecumseh had taken the seat indicated, Brock continued: "We had arrived at the point in the discussion where we are considering future strategy. General Hull's reluctance to move from Sandwich, and his subsequent retreat to Detroit have left us—luckily—with an advantage. If we move quickly we may be able to strengthen our position. Your suggestions would be welcome."

Tecumseh stared into the shimmering fire for a moment. Then he said quietly, "If I were asked the best way, I would say—attack Detroit at once!"

Brock's eyebrows lifted in surprise. A startled exclamation rose throughout the room, capped by Colonel Procter's vehement: "Oh, I *say*! The savage is mad!"

Brock lifted one hand. "Wait! Hear him out!"

Tecumseh glanced about, drawing his knife. "Is there something upon which I could sketch a map?"

One of the officers passed up a piece of elm bark from the fireplace.

Quickly and deftly the point of Tecumseh's knife inscribed the plan of Fort Detroit on the bark. He had scouted the American fort and knew it well, and he gave Brock a rapid and accurate summary of its defense. The general listened attentively. When Tecumseh had outlined his plan, he concluded:

"Half the battle is already won for us, since General Hull is plainly a coward. The very dispatches I captured—written by his own people at Detroit—said as much. Such a man would be terrified by a sudden attack."

"Nonsense!" Procter snorted. "We would be butchered."

"One moment," Brock said quietly. "Let us put it to a vote."

Tecumseh, aglow with triumph, suddenly saw his plan defeated. One officer only—the army's quartermaster—voted in favor. Brock cast no vote. When the count had been taken, Brock sighed and stood up.

"Gentlemen, I am very sorry to override you, but I believe you are wrong and that our Shawnee friend is right. It is, assuredly, a gamble. But all battles are gambles. The prize is exceedingly attractive." Brock's voice hardened. "Tomorrow we shall mount an attack against Fort Detroit. Shooting Star, assemble your people at dawn, for I wish to speak personally to them of the attack." He stared at the ring of silent, astonished faces. "That is all, gentlemen. To your stations. The army must be ready to move by noon tomorrow!"

Chairs crashed over. Voices rose. The officers scrambled into action. Filled with admiration, Tecumseh stared at Brock for a long moment. Then he turned, and with Shabbona at his heels, hurried back through the lightly falling rain to the camp of his people.

15. THE GUNS OF DETROIT

A great thick oak tree, gnarled by time, towered and spread its branches over the broad meadow just outside Amherstburg. Beneath the massive limbs General Isaac Brock faced a thousand of Tecumseh's finest warriors. An oppressive morning mist lay over the meadow, and the braves stood silently while it swirled about their feet, making them a savagely painted army of ghosts. Tecumseh smiled in deep satisfaction as Brock stepped forward. An interpreter swiftly translated his words:

"You, the noble friends of Chief Tecumseh, are comrades of whom I am most proud. I welcome you into the army of our father, the Great King."

A ripple of pleasure, deep in the throats of the braves, swept the meadow. Tecumseh cast a sidelong glance at the other British officers. His eyes lingered on Colonel Procter, who stared at his boots.

"My message this morning is brief," Brock continued. "Your leader has shown me the wisdom of carrying the fight across the water. We plan to attack Fort Detroit, and if you accompany my soldiers, I promise we shall all be fighting together with one aim—to drive out the Americans and regain the lands which they stole from you. As symbol of my faith and respect. . ."

Here Brock drew from beneath his scarlet tunic a handsome silver gorget, on which the head of a man had been engraved.

". . . I ask Chief Tecumseh whether he will wear this medallion, which bears the face of our leader, His Majesty King George III." Brock turned, holding the wampum string that formed the necklace upon which the medallion was hung.

"Will you wear the symbol of my king next to your heart, Shooting Star?"

Slowly Tecumseh nodded. "My battle is yours, my brother." He bowed his head. Brock placed the gorget with its wampum cord over the Shawnee's muscled neck.

And on that afternoon, the fourteenth of August, General Isaac Brock and Tecumseh of the Shawnee led the army north toward the town of Sandwich.

From his headquarters in an imposing brick house, Brock guided the arrangement of artillery. Cannon were hauled up along the river's shore, behind a screen of trees. Artillery officers busily computed the range and elevation required to send hundreds of pounds of iron smashing down upon the American fort.

Tecumseh conferred briefly with his new leader, then gathered a party of six hundred warriors as night fell upon the Detroit. Silently his small army crossed the river below Sandwich, then crept through the murmuring summer darkness until a solid line of tomahawks and long rifles ringed Fort Detroit. All through the night Tecumseh moved up and down this line, watching the activity behind the American stockade. Eerie signals were hooted in the darkness. Many a sentry along the fort walls turned, cocked his head, listened to the strange piercing cries of what seemed to be wild turkey and coyote in the dark, whispering forest.

The next day Brock sent a courier across the river with a written demand that General Hull surrender. At the same time axes rang out, cutting away the screen of oak trees. Their aim cleared, the cannon roared. The bombardment of Fort Detroit had begun.

Through the long, hot night the cannon spoke. Shortly past dawn of the following day Brock and seven hundred troops boated across the Detroit under a blazing artillery cover. At noon Brock called Tecumseh to him and explained a plan he had already put into action—a messenger had been purposely sent too near the walls of Fort Detroit. By this time he had surely been captured. The man carried a forged dispatch to Brock which reported that a war party of five thousand Indians was descending from Michilimackinac Island to aid the British.

Tecumseh nodded approval of the plan. The sun grew hotter in the forest. The cannon on the Canadian shore kept up the firing. Roofs were burning now within Fort Detroit, and answering cannon fire was sporadic. But there was no sign of surrender. Tecumseh had his first doubts that perhaps his plan had been rash.

As the afternoon wore on, Tecumseh was joined by a British lieutenant urging him to meet Brock immediately half a mile away along a wooden trail. Tecumseh turned and headed his gray mustang back up the trail. He found Brock scowling at a sweating, deerskin-clad scout in the remote clearing where the cannon echoed dimly.

"There is trouble?" Tecumseh asked.

Brock nodded. "It appears an American force is just three miles to the south of us and moving up rapidly. Our scouts were taken by surprise. At any rate, this supply train, with provisions *and* armed troops, will be on us in a short while. We'll be trapped between their lines and the fort unless we can crack Hull's defenses in a space of thirty minutes."

Tecumseh's brows knotted. "Let me think a moment. . . that forged dispatch. . . !"

Brock raised his eyes questioningly. Suddenly Tecumseh smiled. He bent forward earnestly, speaking in haste.

Down the lines the signal passed. And almost at once, every throat, white and red, vibrated with the most terrifyingly savage whoops. Astride his mustang, calling quick orders, Tecumseh sent his six hundred warriors running four and five abreast across a broad clearing near the walls of the fort. The running line of men twisted back through the forest in a circle, and just as the end of the column vanished from sight, the leaders appeared in the clearing once more. Heads popped over the top of the American stockade. The cannon boomed from the Canadian shore. The air rang with murderous cries. And a third time the six hundred bolted through the clearing, until it must have seemed to the terrified eyes of the Americans that every savage on the North American continent was out there in the forest.

Brock sat his horse near Tecumseh, breathlessly waiting, hand on his sword hilt, ready to call for a charge should the ruse fail.

With a cry Tecumseh pointed upward. "There! Hull shows his colors! Our trick army has deceived him!"

It was true. Up the flagstaff of the fort moved a snapping banner of white cloth.

Brock laughed with pleasure and clapped Tecumseh's shoulder in admiration. He inclined his head and together he and Tecumseh rode forward toward the gates of Fort Detroit, which were beginning to swing slowly open.

Thus the British flag was raised above the American town because of General Hull's cowardice, and because of the cunning of Tecumseh.

As Tecumseh and Brock rode into the conquered town, the Americans stared at them, shocked and humiliated by defeat, surprised and astonished at the suddenness of it all. Behind the two leaders, red and white, came the British regulars and Tecumseh's braves, pouring inside the walls, shouting, cheering.

In that year Fort Detroit was a fur-trading capital of the Northwest. Eight hundred people lived there, in addition to the American troops. French was spoken almost exclusively by the citizens, and the strange language pleased Tecumseh's ear as he moved about in the streets. After the formalities of surrender had been completed with General Hull, Tecumseh's warriors returned to make camp outside the walls. Brock established his headquarters in a house on Jefferson Street, and Tecumseh was given a parlor and bedroom on the second floor.

That evening Tecumseh sat in his parlor in a large, ornate wing chair, which felt peculiar and enjoyable at the same time. He had never been accorded such fine treatment before, and his quartering in such a luxurious place was evidence of Brock's pleasure. This also pleased the Shawnee. Yet he could not help feeling a bit uneasy, for while he had been in the house of whites many times, he was now established in a white man's house himself, and he felt as though he should be with his warriors, amidst more familiar objects and surroundings.

A fire burned on the hearth. From the street there came a howl and a clatter as one of his warriors jolted through the town in a captured carriage. But Tecumseh knew Shabbona would keep order. He had given strict instructions against looting and scalping.

Brock entered the room, pulled off his boots and sank into a chair, exhausted. Tecumseh passed the pipe he was smoking, and the general drew on it with relish. Then he smiled warmly at his companion.

"There is a look of pleasure on your face, my friend."

"I am at peace tonight," Tecumseh told him. "This has not happened in many years. Perhaps it is because today was so very good, and the battle went well." Speaking in English, he added, "Perhaps it is because I have fought beside a noble soldier."

"Come now, you're the one the Yankees are calling noble," Brock answered with a laugh. "Why, wherever the citizens or the captured troops gather one hears a single name—Tecumseh. Not one American has been attacked or molested in any way by your people. They imagined they would all be parted from their hair, I suppose. Procter as much as said you'd bathe in the blood of the poor prisoners."

"Procter is very foolish. My people are not always easily controlled. But there will be neither peace nor honor for them until they walk as men, not animals. This lesson I have tried to teach those who fight with me."

"There's been no drinking, no violence. They have behaved admirably. I wish all war could be as bloodless. And I only regret I cannot stay here longer."

Tecumseh leaned forward in the firelight. "You are leaving?"

"Tomorrow, yes. I must. There is danger of invasion on the Niagara border."

"Then in this moment I am no longer at peace."

"You mean because of Procter? Don't concern yourself. I've spoken to him—and besides, I believe you actually impressed that pompous oaf this afternoon."

But General Isaac Brock's words did not calm Tecumseh, nor bring a dreamless sleep. His moment of peace passed as quickly as it had come, and in the morning he felt Procter watching him smugly while Brock took his leave in an elaborate presentation ceremony. Tecumseh received a brilliant silken sash and a pair of expensive pistols from the British general, and in return he gave Brock a six-foot wampum belt of the finest workmanship.

Brock extended his hand. "I hope we shall meet again soon, Shooting Star."

"I hope also," Tecumseh echoed, though with uncertainty.

Brock was gone as swiftly as he had come. . . and trouble descended twenty-four hours after the gates closed behind him.

Tecumseh learned of it from Billy Caldwell, in the parlor of the house on Jefferson Street. On taking command, Colonel Procter had immediately issued an order requiring all citizens of Detroit to swear an oath of loyalty to King George. Father Gabriel Richard, a Catholic missionary priest, refused to submit to the oath, vowing he would pledge allegiance only to the American Constitution. Father Richard, Caldwell reported, had been speedily taken across the river to Sandwich and clapped behind bars.

When Tecumseh heard of this he strode through the gathering twilight to Procter's headquarters. With several guards whom he had ignored trailing behind, he burst into Procter's lamplit office. The colonel, his red face unhealthy with perspiration, looked up from his quill and paper and sighed in annoyance.

"My dear chief," he said with badly hidden contempt, "I am occupied by many pressing matters. I have no time to talk . . ."

Tecumseh reached out and snapped the quill pen in half. Procter gasped and fumed, held speechless by Tecumseh's anger.

"You will release Father Richard from the Sandwich prison."

"What? Now see here—!" Procter rose to his feet. "I resent your tone! The Jesuit refused to swear to the oath—"

"He is skilled in the medical arts," Tecumseh said sharply. "This has been told to me. There are Americans wounded by the cannon fire before the surrender whom the holy man has been tending. They need his care."

"He will not be released. That is final!"

Tecumseh hesitated. "Very well. Then hold Fort Detroit with your little army of whites. . . alone."

Procter's eyes bulged. "W—what?"

"If you do not release Richard before the eye of the sun clears the rim of the earth, my people and I shall be gone to the Wabash."

"You—you wouldn't dare leave me here."

"General Brock would understand my reasons."

Colonel Procter grew suddenly pale. He shot a hateful glance at Tecumseh, turned his back and grunted, "Very well. Richard will be released. Now get out."

Tecumseh marched from the office, pleased with his success. He had done what had to be done—what was right. But the interview had totally destroyed his confidence in the future success of the war.

Tecumseh did not remain long in Fort Detroit. He moved southward with his army of warriors, and for twelve days surrounded Fort Wayne, but without success. The fort was sturdily built, its troops well provisioned. Tecumseh had difficulty supplying food for his own force while maintaining the siege. Then a messenger from Procter arrived, recalling him to Fort Malden.

News traveled slowly in time of war on the frontier. Procter had received word from Brock that an armistice had been reached, beginning the twenty-seventh of June—long before Detroit was captured. Tecumseh later learned that the same armistice had ended on the twenty-ninth of August. He pondered deeply upon a course of action, and sent word that he would not return to Amherstburg.

As he saw it, the problem was splitting the American forces. He knew that he must continue to fight near the Great Lakes, because there his people could receive supplies from the British. But he reasoned that the British could also provision the southern tribes from bases on the Gulf of Mexico. So if the torch could be lit below the mountains, the Long Knives would have to fight two wars instead of one. In that way there might be a greater chance for success.

The victory at Detroit was proof that the Americans could be defeated. Swiftly Tecumseh dispatched messengers to the Creek to spread the news of his coming. And then, in September of 1812—for the last time—he wearily turned his face southward on another long journey.

16. THE SCALP-TAKERS

Tecumseh stood with a tomahawk in his hand, a tomahawk whose head and shaft had been colored red by vegetable dyes. Its color stood out brilliantly in the smoke-filled council house of the Upper Creek, a bloody color amidst the twisting smoke whorls from a few pitch pine torches.

The hour was midnight. Nearly a hundred warriors and chiefs of the Upper Creek sat in a circle, while Tecumseh stood in the center of the ring they formed, facing the greatest leader of them all, the young Red Eagle—William Weatherford, the half-breed. Sweat stood out on Tecumseh's body, turning him to a gleaming bronzed statue. He had been speaking for half an hour at this secret council session, and now his voice rose impassionedly:

"Why not vanquish the Long Knives and free ourselves from their yoke, their schools, their spinning wheels, their plows and clothing—these emblems of our subjugation and disgrace? These fetters on our limbs and our freedom?

"Why doubt our power to defeat them? We have done it in the North, we have conquered the fortress of Detroit. Our father, the Great King over the water, will never bend our backs to his burden. Our villages will be safe from the despoiler, and our hunting grounds will again be as free as the arrow in the air, free as the flight of the eagle in the sky. The Americans we ıust fight. The Americans are our eternal foes, the hungry levourers of the country of our fathers."

Tecumseh paused, breathing deeply. Weatherford's hawkish 'oung face showed grim resolve. Tecumseh said, "I ask the ;reek for war." And he extended the red tomahawk.

Weatherford slowly let his gaze travel around the council .ouse. Tecumseh felt a swelling sense of triumph. Catlike, Veatherford came to his feet, his hand closing over the offered ɔmahawk.

"The Creek seize the red tomahawk," he said. "The Creek ıave answered their brother Tecumseh. *The Creek pledge war.*"

In the spring of the year following the battle of Fort Detroit, 'ecumseh was again moving north along the Wabash, this time ;athering his finest, most savage army behind him. With Shab-ona pausing along the way to recruit large bands of warriors, 'ecumseh's confidence was renewed. In Weatherford Tecumseh elt he had found a comrade who could lead the Creek effec-ively, yet who was able to exercise firm control over his people, o that the coming struggle in the South would be a carefully xecuted attack, not merely a series of senseless and brutal bat-les which did more harm than good to the cause of the red man.

Three thousand warriors streamed out behind Tecumseh when ıe entered Fort Malden in April of 1813. Shortly afterward he 'eceived grim news from Colonel Elliot.

Sitting by the fire where they counciled in Tecumseh's wig-vam, Matthew Elliot said slowly, "Your comrade General Brock s dead."

The Shawnee leader raised eyes filled with pain. "When did his happen?"

"Last year. The thirteenth of October, to be exact. He died in ɔattle, leading his men at Queenston Heights, near Niagara."

"And who is in command here?" Tecumseh's tone grew ɔminous.

Elliot smiled sourly. “Procter, of course. Major *General* Procter,” he added, emphasizing the promotion.

Tecumseh gazed angrily into the fire. “Then the confederation is in danger.”

“Why do you say that?”

“Brock would have understood what I planned for my people Procter will dismiss my pleas with a sneer. I believed that Brock saw my people as they are—humane, courageous, capable o governing themselves wisely. Procter thinks of us as savages.”

There was a rueful expression on Matthew Elliot's face then “I am afraid, Shooting Star, that impression was strengthened while you were gone from us.”

“Explain what you mean, Elliot.”

Reluctantly the Indian agent told the story: on the previou twenty-second of January, General Procter and a band of brave under Roundhead attacked eight hundred Americans at Frenchtown, on the Raisin River. Most of the Long Knives had been killed or captured in the fight, and some sixty-five wounded Americans had been left behind in the snow while Procter returned to the fort.

“Procter promised protection for these wounded,” Ellio stated. “He intended to send sleds for them, but even before the main force had reached Malden, Roundhead and a group o braves crept back to the camp of the wounded. They had been drinking. Roundhead's warriors fell on the wounded men. . .”

“Do not hesitate to finish the story,” Tecumseh said ominously. “Tell me what the weakling Roundhead did.”

“It was because of the liquor. . .” Elliot hedged.

“Tell me!”

“Every last wounded man was scalped.”

Elliot's eyes showed the horror of it. “I reached the camp day after the attack. There was so much blood upon the snow that . . . that . . ." He passed a hand across his eyes, shook his head. He could not continue.

Tecumseh leaped to his feet. He raced outside. "Shabbona! Shabbona!" His voice trembled with rage. Shabbona came trotting up through the darkness. Tecumseh said softly. "Bring Roundhead to me."

At dawn the air was split with the shrill cries of Roundhead and the other warriors who had been on the scalping party. Their backs felt the sting of a deerhide lash administered by Shabbona; and though Tecumseh was revolted by the punishment which he himself had ordered, he felt deeply that an example must be set. Surely Roundhead's brutality had done immeasurable harm to the cause of the union of the tribes. All the respect Procter might have felt for the tribes after Fort Detroit had been wiped out by the childish and heartless slaughter of helpless wounded soldiers.

That April Procter ordered Tecumseh's people to march with him to the rapids of the Maumee River, in the Ohio land, where Harrison had swiftly built Fort Meigs, directly opposite the site of Fallen Timbers. All across the frontier the whites were rising to strike back at the warring tribes, and Harrison had been placed at the head of the armies in the West. He was hidden behind the walls of Fort Meigs with twelve hundred troops, awaiting the arrival of General Green Clay's one thousand men already moving up from the south.

Tecumseh and Procter marched on Fort Meigs with roughly twenty-five hundred men, of which only a thousand were British soldiers. On the twenty-fifth of April the two leaders rode out ahead and surveyed Fort Meigs from the woods near Fallen Timbers. Procter peered through a spyglass, noting the heavy concentrations of Americans along the walls—not only regular soldiers, but settlers in coonskin caps and linsey-woolsey clothing who had joined Harrison against the menace of the tribes.

Surveying the situation, Tecumseh spoke: "I have a plan which I think would bring the Long Knives from the fort so that we might attack."

"Never mind, never mind!" Procter replied in irritation. "I am quite capable of planning the strategy of this campaign. Please remember that I am in command, and that I have had the benefit of professional military training."

Tecumseh turned pale at the new insult. Procter wheeled his gelding and clattered away through the forest.

On the following day the English soldiers boated up the Maumee River in small craft and proceeded to set up artillery batteries to fire on Fort Meigs from the north. At that time it was quite easy for Procter to move heavy cannon into the river, for the British virtually controlled Lake Erie. Forcing himself to obey Procter for the good of the campaign, Tecumseh moved his warriors to the south of the fort, taking up a position along the line of march of Clay's brigade which was approaching from the south. From May first until May third Procter's cannon hammered mercilessly at the fort, but his message calling for surrender was swiftly rejected by Harrison.

Enraged at the way General Harrison hid safely behind the walls, Tecumseh himself sent an angry message to the American commander demanding that he abandon his cowardly tactics and fight in the open. No answer came from the fort. Tecumseh's rage increased so much that when General Clay's brigade drew within striking distance, he was ready for battle. He led his warriors in the attack with a fury that made his men believe he was possessed of some sort of devil. In the fight that raged along the shore of the Maumee, four hundred and fifty Americans were killed, one hundred and fifty were captured and the rest slipped across the river to sanctuary within the gates of Fort Meigs.

Riding through the wilderness of fallen trees after the battle,

Tecumseh suddenly came upon a scene that sent his temper flaming once more.

Three dozen American soldiers, many of them lying wounded, were grouped in a circle vainly trying to fight off nearly twice as many red men. Tecumseh's eyes took in the gory sight of those prisoners who had already been scalped. His ears heard the terrified cries of new victims as the warriors lifted their knives in the sunlight. Uttering a hoarse shout, he urged his mount forward and flung himself off the animal's back in the center of the clearing.

He tore the scalp knife from the hand of one warrior and flung it away. When another stepped forward in protest, Tecumseh's hands crashed down, sending him sprawling. Those prisoners left alive watched the Shawnee in awe, as he stalked from warrior to warrior, ruthlessly cuffing each face.

"Are you honorable men? Or beasts? Are you human beings? Or stupid, crazed animals? I should take the knife to all of you, for doing such a wicked and heartless thing!"

The red men drifted away, cowed by Tecumseh's words. When the Shawnee leader made certain the wounded were turned over to a squad of regular British troops, he rode to find Procter, suddenly filled with sadness. For the first time he doubted that his people could ever really earn the right to be treated fairly by the whites. If they could not give up their brutal desires to butcher and mutilate defenseless prisoners, then how could they ever grasp the ideas he had been trying to make them understand? How could they form a union of tribes which would be strong, powerful and—most important—wise? Sadly, as he rode through the smoking battleground, he said to himself, *They cannot. It cannot be done!*

He felt defeated. He had struggled for nothing; the cause was lost.

Nevertheless, he demanded satisfaction from Procter. He

stormed into the Britisher's campaign tent, exclaiming, "I am but one man, and the battlefield is large. I cannot be at all places at all times. Why have you not instructed your troops to hold my people with a firm hand, as I asked many times? You could stop slaughter such as I now witnessed."

He quickly narrated the revolting details of the scalping, his voice becoming a roar.

"I asked that you give orders to your soldiers to guard against such happenings! I asked not once, but many times!"

"My dear fellow," Procter said, concentrating on writing a dispatch on his field table. "I realize you requested that I do something of the sort, but I felt an order of that type was foolish.

He lifted his eyes contemptuously. "Your people are simple. They will not listen to the same appeals which strike a chord with reasonable men. They are impossible to control. They do not understand; they are not civilized."

Tecumseh's mouth curled. "*I* brought them under control!" he shouted, crashing a fist down on the flimsy table. "*I* stopped the brutality! But *you* would not issue the order because you are frightened. You dress in the clothing of a man, but you are not a man—you are a *squaw*!"

Procter was white with rage, but Tecumseh did not wait for his reply. He rushed from the tent in despair.

On the ninth day of May, 1813, the siege of Fort Meigs was withdrawn because no reinforcements were available, and because Procter saw no means of budging the entrenched Americans from within the stout walls. The British troops and Indians retreated to Malden, where a long, saddening summer set in.

Singly, then by twos and threes, then by tens and twenties, the red men began to drift away, back to the cool trails of the woods, back to their families. Tecumseh and Shabbona tried vainly to stop them, but they knew the reason behind the desertions: the warriors had caught the scent of contempt that hovered like bitter perfume around General Procter. They knew he considered them unfit to fight beside the British troops, and his dislike was shown openly by his treatment of them. When the Britishers received a ration of beef, Tecumseh discovered that Procter had ordered horsemeat for the Indians. There was another bitter scene between them, and Tecumseh's army received the beef he demanded, but Procter's hatred of the Shawnee leader grew still stronger.

Over the Great Lakes that summer the war clouds were rolling in to bring a last, fateful climax to the battle for the northwest frontier.

At Erie, Pennsylvania, Commodore Oliver Hazard Perry, an American naval officer, was struggling to build ships . . . to build an American fighting navy that could win control of the lakes from the British and cut the line of supply which kept Fort Malden in food and ammunition. Tecumseh heard the news spies brought of this fleet. He bitterly reflected that had General Brock been alive he would have lost no time attacking the fleet while it was still under construction. But Procter's answer was to build a single vessel, the *Detroit*, with the help of British shipwrights who had journeyed across the lakes earlier that summer.

The *Detroit* was in fact a splendid vessel, a brig of nearly five hundred tons, and the man who supervised her construction, Captain Robert Barclay, was reputed to be an excellent naval officer. One sleeve of his uniform was pinned up at the shoulder, token of his service with Lord Nelson at Trafalgar. The red men looked on the *Detroit* as a magical and mighty craft. Toward the end, as the time for launching neared, Tecumseh also began to hope that the battle would be successful. For it was certain that a battle *was* approaching. Even the Indians could interpret the rumors flying through the air that summer: there would be a great fight upon the waters, and it would be the one chance for the Americans to take control of a strategic portion of the Northwest.

It was called the Battle of Put-in-Bay, and it took place on September 10, 1813.

All through that day Tecumseh and hundreds of his followers crouched silently on Bois Blanc Island, listening. The roar of cannon could be heard across the water, more than a hundred miles away. The Indian leader wished that he could be on the *Detroit,* seeing how the battle fared.

When Barclay's ships blasted Perry's flagship the *Lawrence* out of action, the Americans refused to turn away and give up the fight. A chance change in wind drifted the *Lawrence* toward her sister ship, the *Niagara,* and Perry swiftly transferred his colors. Barclay had been wounded in the battle and could no longer command as the cannon roared again. By the time night fell, the British fleet had been blasted. The British stranglehold on the northern lakes was broken.

No whisper of cannon fire reached Bois Blanc that night.

A strange, deathly silence hung over Fort Malden. The *Detroit* did not appear on the horizon at dawn, as expected. The Indians grew restless. The long, smooth gray line of Lake Erie was unbroken. Still, it was possible, they thought, that Barclay was pursuing the fight farther along the lakes.

Suddenly there was activity as runners crossed the Detroit River to the fort. Tecumseh waited among his people. Procter did not send for him. At last the Shawnee could stand the uncertainty no longer, and he went to the general's quarters.

"What of the battle upon the water?" he asked.

"Oh . . ." Procter shrugged. "There has been little news."

"Where is Barclay? Where is the *Detroit*?"

The general concentrated on some papers. "I'm quite busy at the moment."

"Was the battle won?"

Procter licked his lips nervously. His eyes moved sideways. "Let us say that . . . ah . . . the outcome was satisfactory."

"What does that mean? Will you give me a straight answer? Will you tell me if Barclay won?"

"You must excuse me," the Britisher said hastily, hurrying from the room.

Tecumseh stepped out into the sunlight, pondering. Procter had tried to suggest a victory, yet he had displayed too much nervousness. If Barclay had indeed won, there should have been jubilation.

The chief's eyes suddenly narrowed, and he broke into a run toward the general's personal quarters, where a handsome carriage was drawn up. Two soldiers were straining to lift a heavy trunk onto it. Tecumseh recognized the carriage as the one in which Procter used to ride about Amherstburg.

"What are you doing?" he shouted to the soldiers. "Why are you loading these things?"

The men exchanged amused glances. One of them laughed, a bit grimly.

"Why, bucko, we're loading up all the general's pretty dress uniforms. We hear he's planning to take a little trip. We hear he wants to get as far away from this place as his fancy team of grays can take him. Considers the fort unhealthy all of a sudden, so it seems."

While the two men laughed again at Tecumseh's question, the Shawnee felt a cold, hard knot of fear tighten his stomach. A trickle of clammy perspiration ran down his neck.

He did not need to be told the truth about the naval engagement now. There was no *Detroit* in the river. The cannon were silent.

And Procter was throwing his belongings into his carriage as quickly as possible, ready to retreat because the battle had been lost.

17. DISHONOR'S ROAD

At dawn the following morning, long, silent lines of warriors slipped toward the bluff overlooking the Detroit River. They moved through the mist with scarcely a sound, for Tecumseh's call to gather had struck a terrified note in their hearts. Shabbona stood near the head of the throng, a cheap cotton blanket of British issue around his shoulders, a frown of worry on his face. Tecumseh approached slowly through the drifting fog.

Shabbona's heart felt a stab of sorrow. How gaunt the Shawnee looked! How tired, how defeated. Though he was forty-five summers, that morning of September twelfth Tecumseh seemed to have shriveled into a weary, worn old man.

Slowly he mounted a large boulder on the edge of the bluff. He was about to speak when a clatter of hoofs and a rattle of wheels cut through the mist. Shabbona turned sharply. Procter's carriage came to a halt at the edge of the parade ground. The fat general sat inside, muffled in a heavy coat. He cowered as though he must hear Tecumseh's words at any cost, even though he feared drawing too close to the mutinous Indians.

"My people," Tecumseh said slowly, "the ships of the Great King went out from this place, but they do not return. They have been destroyed. We heard the thunder on the distant water, and it was the thunder of defeat. There is an army of Long Knives marching north through the forest to strike us. But as they march, the leader of the Great King's soldiers already gathers his goods and prepares to flee, afraid for his life. If he is a coward, and if his men are cowards, then I ask that they leave us their weapons, so that we may fight the Long Knives when they cross the river."

An angry growl of agreement rippled through the crowd. As quickly as he had come, Procter disappeared, rushing back to the safety of his quarters, afraid to hear more of the accusing voice rolling out across the parade ground.

"If the white man Procter is a coward," the Shawnee went on, "we are not cowards, and with his guns we can still fight as honorable men!"

Before the morning sun had risen far into the sky, Tecumseh's strong words on the parade ground drew an unexpected response. Major Muir invited the Shawnee leader to a hastily called council in Procter's rooms. Tecumseh and Shabbona entered haughtily. The red-faced, frightened general hardly dared look them in the eye, for he feared the strong force of braves gathered at his fort. While the senior British officers took chairs, Tecumseh indicated that he wished to stand, and said simply:

"I came to the house of the Great King to fight, not to run."

"At the moment," Procter hedged nervously, "it seems more strategic to withdraw to the northeast, in the hope that some future action. . ."

"Words!" Tecumseh said sharply. "Empty words hide the coward's way."

"Just a moment!" Procter exclaimed, staggering to his feet. But his bluff died on his lips when he gazed into the terrible and bitter eyes of Tecumseh.

The chief said quietly: "I will fight. You will fight with me."

Procter licked his lips. He glanced about at his senior officers who waited anxiously. He had to solve the dilemma by himself. At last he spoke weakly, "What if we agree to fall back to the

Thames River and make our defense near Chatham? Or perhaps near Moraviantown? Would you find that satisfactory?"

For a long moment Tecumseh fixed Procter with a withering gaze. Then he turned abruptly, signaled Shabbona and marched from the room. Procter fell into a chair, mopping perspiration from his face. "Evidently that satisfied the red man," someone muttered, but Procter did not hear. He was staring dumbly at the tips of his boots, sick with uncertainty and terror.

Cutting northward like an avenging blade came the army of William Henry Harrison and Governor Isaac Shelby of Kentucky. On the nineteenth of September, Procter's troops left Malden behind, putting it to the torch, leaving it as a smoldering monument of defeat. The British moved north to Sandwich, with Tecumseh and his braves following close behind.

The following day the American army of five thousand soldiers eager for battle boarded Commodore Perry's ships and started across Lake Erie for the invasion of Canada. At the same time, swinging around the rim of the lake, came fifteen hundred cavalry—the two elements forming a vast military engine designed to crush the forces of George III before it.

On the night of September twenty-seventh, a sumptuous dinner was set by candlelight in the home of the fur trader Jacques Baby at Sandwich. The finest venison and wild fowl were placed before General Procter and his officers. Tecumseh arrived late, having decided to accept the general's grudging invitation so that he could keep the Britisher constantly aware of his promise to fight.

Procter blanched when the Shawnee took his seat at the table and placed the pistols which Brock had given him on either side of his plate. He then laid a scalping knife, gleaming wickedly in the candle glow, above one of the pistols. Then he concentrated on his food, taking no part in the conversation which went on about him.

"I was moving through Ohio, y'know, in buckskin, watching

the Yankees and so forth, and I happened to be in this little village called Xenia," someone was saying. Dimly Tecumseh heard the words spoken by Colonel Fonteyn, newly arrived that morning after several weeks of dangerous spying in enemy country. "Caught sight of one of the most beautiful women I've ever seen."

"Oh, come now, Fonteyn, that's merely the result of living by yourself so long. All women appear beautiful."

"No, this lady *was* beautiful. No one paid any attention to me, don't y'see, because there was a wedding being performed that day. Oh, yes, a wedding, in spite of all the upset, armies marching and whatnot. This woman was truly a vision in her bridal gown," Fonteyn bantered lightly. "Anyway, Muir, if you could have seen this Galloway girl, for that was her name. . ."

Tecumseh raised his head. *"Galloway?"*

Colonel Fonteyn swiveled around, startled. "Why, yes. Rebecca Galloway, that's what they said her name was, in the crowd outside the little chapel. You know her?"

"No," Tecumseh replied hoarsely. "No. It is a pretty name, that is all."

"Oh." Fonteyn shrugged. "Well, Muir, as I was saying. . ."

"Did she marry a white man?" Tecumseh asked suddenly.

"Why, of course," Fonteyn replied, amused; then he resumed his talk. But for Tecumseh, the last dark cup of bitterness had reached his lips.

Rebecca!

The name sang in his tired mind like ancient chords of sweet music. How lovely she had been, and how dear to him. But lost like his vision of a great Indian confederation—lost in the past, in a hundred mistakes, an endless chain of circumstances which had brought him here like a tame animal, munching venison from a plate in a white man's house, in a company of cowards commanded by the greatest coward of them all. Not fighting, not struggling for what he believed, but eating like a stupid, placid cow, while in the dark night to the south the Long Knife army rolled on, huge, sprawling, powerful, bent on destruction.

Procter simpered over some jest of Major Muir's. Colonel Fonteyn chuckled and dabbed his lips with a napkin. A dinner, an empty feast . . . news of Rebecca . . . defeat . . . the plans, the dreams that were dying. Tecumseh's heart cried out in anguish. He felt enveloped in a cold wind that enshrouded him, hooted at him, mocked . . . a wind of defeat, a wind of death. . .

Then suddenly there was a hammering at the door of the dining room. A moment later a red-coated sergeant burst in, eyes popping, breathing hard.

"General Procter!" he stammered. "The American ships are coming up the river . . . our lookout saw. . ."

He was interrupted by a breaking of glass as Procter leaped to his feet and upset a goblet. "How many vessels?"

"Fifteen or sixteen, sir. And small craft. The river is black with them."

"We must move out of Sandwich immediately!" the general cried.

"What is to prevent us from fighting here tonight?" Tecumseh demanded.

"We fight when I decide to fight!" Procter piped hysterically, rushing to the door. "Hurry, Major Muir, for God's sake!"

The front door of the house slammed open as the British officers hurried into the night, and a wild wind suddenly swept through the dining room. Another glass fell over with a crash.

Chilled to the bone, Tecumseh watched while the candles in their holders blew out one by one in the rising wind.

The British army broke from Sandwich that night in panic, streaming out to the west toward the Thames River. Tecumseh and his thousand warriors—all that were left of his once-mighty force—trailed swiftly behind through the darkness and following dawn, moving through the Canadian wilderness with a dedicated leader at their head. Though the great Shawnee felt beaten in his dream of an Indian confederation, he was determined to fight—instead of running like a terrified beast.

As Perry's ships came sailing into Lake St. Clair, Tecumseh's warriors were straggling into the small village of log cabins and a single blockhouse that was Chatham. The sound of the Long Knife army could be heard not far behind. William Henry Harrison and his thirty-five hundred soldiers were coming up fast. The battle would have to come now! But Procter had already gone up the road to Moraviantown, flying along in his carriage loaded with baggage, more than twenty miles beyond the village where Tecumseh had decided they must fight.

In what little heat the chilly noon sunlight offered, the tag ends of the British force rested in Chatham—seven hundred men of the First Battalion of the Forty-first Line Regiment. Their commander was Colonel Warburton, a proper, formally trained soldier. Tecumseh found him at a hastily made cook fire with several of his officers. Though the chief's deerskin shirt and trousers were stained with dirt and ripped in a dozen places, he still presented an imposing sight as he stalked before Warburton and pointed toward the west, a fierce expression on his tired but proud features.

"Harrison is coming," he declared. "We fight here."

Warburton wiped a grimy scarlet sleeve across his nose. "For heaven's sake, man, you know we can't stop. We would be wiped out!"

"If Procter had set fire to the bridges behind us we would have time," Tecumseh speculated grimly. "But the bridges still stand, and the Long Knives rush across them. Soon they will catch us, but they shall not see my back. They shall look in my face; we will turn and fight!"

Warburton bristled importantly. "See here, you! I take orders from no one but General Procter!"

"Who is already traveling far ahead, out of the path of danger. This is a road of dishonor which we march upon because Procter has made it so. I will remain here and fight, so that some of the evil stain of cowardice is washed away. I am not afraid to die," Tecumseh said slowly. "I would rather die honorably than like a whipped dog."

Colonel Warburton's spine stiffened. "Are you implying. . ."

"Will you fight?" Tecumseh repeated.

Warburton swallowed. He glanced at his tired men sprawled beneath leafless trees.

"All right," he said with determination. "Yes, all right, I'll stand with you."

A smile spread on Tecumseh's face, but it was not a happy smile. It was only tiredly satisfied.

The ragged line of soldiers and warriors deployed. Before long the first of Harrison's cannon would begin to fill the sky with deadly, destroying iron.

Two bridges spanned the Thames near Chatham. On the night of October second Tecumseh's people held a line of resistance near the bridges, waiting for the Long Knives. Colonel Warburton, however, had had enough of the thought of a hopeless conflict, and like black ghosts the Britishers began to disappear up the road to the east. Bitterly Tecumseh determined to hold the two bridges at all cost, but the advancing American army proved too strong. There was a terrible melee of mounted soldiers against warriors on foot, the air torn with shots and the whistle of grapeshot from the cannon, the screams and grisly yells of the Kentucky frontiersmen in the van of Harrison's army. Tecumseh's arm was struck with a piece of shot, but he kept moving through the battlefield, calling orders to his warriors, vainly trying to stem the flow of cavalry hammering savagely at the bridges from the opposite shore. At last he gave orders for retreat. The numbers ranged against him were too great and he had no opportunity to place his men for a good defense. The Indian army broke and swept eastward.

Late the next morning, Tecumseh and his force rested briefly at Arnold's Mill. Then they set out again, up the road to Moraviantown, with one thought burning in Tecumseh's mind above the smoldering pain from his wounded arm: to find Procter, to make him stop and do battle, using all the troops at his command.

On the night of the fourth of October, camped a few miles west on Moraviantown with Procter not far ahead, Tecumseh heard that Harrison had captured a large portion of Procter's ammunition supply, which was being moved secretly eastward away from the main body of the army. Dismally Tecumseh sat down at a cheerless fire with Shabbona and Billy Caldwell. To the east the fires of the British flickered. Tecumseh knew that in the morning he must find Procter, but tonight he felt dizzy and cold, and he huddled in his robe trying to get warmth into his bones. Suddenly he became so tired that he did not think he could move again. His head spun with a strange dizziness and he swayed. Shabbona's strong arm caught him, preventing him from falling.

"What is wrong, my brother?" the loyal Shabbona cried.

"I am weary, and I feel we shall never leave this ground." Tecumseh raised his eyes slowly. "The battle is very close now."

Shabbona shook his head. "Nothing has been right for us—everything has gone wrong. It is almost as though the Great Spirit has turned his face away. Procter of the British is given to us as a commander. Brock, the tall iron soldier, dies. Our friend and good ally Weatherford. . ." The warrior shuddered and closed his eyes, too stricken to continue.

Roused, Tecumseh whispered, "Weatherford of the Creek? What of him?"

Shabbona and Billy Caldwell exchanged apprehensive glances.

"You have not heard of it?" Caldwell asked.

"No one has told me news of Weatherford," Tecumseh said. "Quickly! What is it? Has the war begun below the mountains?"

"It has." Shabbona nodded grimly. "Couriers reached the leaders of the British not long after sundown—two soldiers who dressed as Long Knives and slipped through the lines of the enemy. I thought you had been told."

"What has Weatherford done?"

Shabbona told him that Chief Weatherford and his Creek had slaughtered five hundred and thirty-six white men, women and children in an attack on Fort Mims. Tecumseh's face hardened, then drained of feeling. Crouching above his pitiful fire in the midst of the dark and alien wilderness, the chill which had touched him at the house of the fur trader in Sandwich crept into his bones again.

Even Weatherford . . . even the mighty Creek warrior whom he had trusted above all other allies, whom he had selected to conduct the war in the South! Even this powerful leader had betrayed him, had let his people fall back into the ways of cruel slaughter.

Yet I must not judge too harshly, his numbed mind cautioned. *I am not acquainted with the circumstances, and even I could not always stay the hands of those among my people who lifted the scalping hatchet. Perhaps Weatherford is not to blame. Perhaps he was wounded or killed in the attack. Perhaps. . .*

But the last feeble structure of his dream had crashed to ruin. There was no longer any hope for his people.

"I am sure now, my brothers," he said at last in a broken voice. "May the Great Spirit welcome us all, for at least we can stand honorably tomorrow while we are destroyed."

18.
BUGLES AT FOUR O'CLOCK

Through the long night, after his comrades had drifted off to troubled sleep, Tecumseh had lain awake, sorting out the threads of his existence and trying to arrange them into a kind of pattern which would speak of purpose and achievement. But it was useless. There was nothing left but the knowledge that a trap was closing swiftly.

On the road which curved near the bank of the Thames River, Tecumseh and Shabbona found General Procter's carriage in front of his tent shortly past down.

Hearing once more the Shawnee's demand for a stand against Harrison's troops, the Englishman was filled with panic.

"No, no! You simply do not understand!" he wailed. He dabbed at his face with a handkerchief while Colonel Elliot turned his head in shame. "We cannot withstand the onslaught of the American army. It is impossible!"

Jowls wet with sweat, eyes popping with fear, the general choked off his words and stared in horror. Tecumseh held a pistol in his hand. Its muzzle was pointed directly at the stomach of the British officer. . .

"Are you going to refuse me again?" the Indian whispered. "I do not believe that you will this time!"

Kneeling down, near to tears, Procter so shamed Colonel Elliot that when he quickly tore the pistol from Tecumseh's grip he suddenly wanted to fire at his commander himself. Nearly out of his mind, Procter crawled to his cot and buried his head in the blanket. Tecumseh stiffened. He felt unclean being near such a frightened creature.

"Even if you kill me," Procter cried, "I will maintain that a battle is wrong!"

"Since there is no chance left for victory," Tecumseh replied, "the only course remaining is honorable defeat. We fight."

"Yes," Procter cried piteously, "Oh, yes, all right. But leave me alone, leave me alone!"

Elliot stepped forward and touched Tecumseh's sleeve. "This is most unwise," he whispered. "It is quite evident that the general is in no condition to organize a battle. We can't have much time left. A few hours at the most."

For an instant Tecumseh's old strength returned, and he said simply, "I can organize the armies."

Gazing into the Shawnee's eyes, Elliot made no reply, for there was authority in the red man's words. Elliot nodded and Tecumseh turned and strode from the tent, while Procter continued his frantic sobbing.

Swiftly Tecumseh set to work, his mind no longer occupied with thoughts of death and failure. The proximity of the American army and the planning required for the battle captured all of his attention. He deployed his warriors and the British into a wide line running northward from the river. Elliot aided him, rounding up the officers, getting the troops settled into the woods. Between the British forces nearest the Thames and another wooded area farther north lay a dense, low, swampy area. By placing his braves beyond this swamp, Tecumseh hoped to split the Long Knife attack into two prongs, and at noon the battle lines were drawn.

That very afternoon Procter had managed to find his way to

his carriage and was already clattering away up the road to Moraviantown.

By three the distant noise of Harrison's army on the march reached the Indian defenders in the woods above the swamp.

At four the bugles of the Kentucky horsemen split the Canadian afternoon, and the first ragged lines of whooping buckskin-clad horsemen charged the woods where the British and the Indians were entrenched.

The Kentucky cavalry plunged among the trees. Behind them came wave after wave of foot soldiers. The air thickened with shots, with screams, with a blue pall of smoke. The British line broke first. White flags began to appear near the river. But Tecumseh seemed to keep moving through the woods like a deadly ghost, a pistol smoking hot in one hand, a knife in the other, his face a mask of sweat and dirt, his voice raised endlessly in shouts of encouragement, calling orders, moving little bands and pockets of braves here and there through the nightmare tangle of charging horses and running soldiers.

Crouching behind a tree as half a dozen horsemen swept past, Shabbona peered through the smoky twilight. The sun was down. The firing came less frequently. Breathing hard, his chest aching, Shabbona listened anxiously for perhaps five minutes. Then, slowly, he laid his head against the trunk of the tree. His shoulders heaved, but there was no sound. The silence was so deep it was as if the world stood still.

But then there did come a sound as Shabbona dropped his tomahawk and wept.

Two horsemen rode across the death-strewn battleground in the first cold, pale light of the next dawn. Side by side, wrapped in heavy coats, their mounts breathing noisily, William Henry Harrison and Oliver Hazard Perry went from warrior to fallen warrior, searching for the one face among all others they wished to find. A bugle piped thinly. The camps of the cavalry and infantry stirred and wakened. The sun crept up. Harrison and Perry rode on, searching for the fallen foe whose name had been a torch across the Northwest, whose dream had helped to fire a war, whose strength had shone splendidly in this last great tribute to sheer courage in the face of certain defeat.

They searched for the body of Tecumseh of the Shawnee, but did not find it by the Thames.

And as the same cold dawn sifted through a glade in the woods five miles from the field of defeat, Shabbona knelt with three other warriors and began to dig at the soft Canadian earth with his hands. Shabbona's mind was deadened by pain and his body sodden with weariness, for after the long night of searching for his leader, there had been the longer agony of finding braves to help with the body, to carry it a safe distance from the Long Knife camp. The body lay on a bed of leaves now, the hands folded on the stomach, but the head which had been crushed and bullet-riddled was covered with a tattered fragment of Shabbona's shirt.

Shabbona and the others dug, and the first random rays of the morning sun touched a gleaming silver medallion on the breast of the dead man, a medallion on which the face of the Great King suddenly burned with white reflected luster, like a star. A bird chirruped and rose up among the leaves toward the sun. Shabbona dug—and prayed aloud.

No stone has ever been found which marks the burial place of Tecumseh, but because the story is written in the book of history there is little need for a stone.

Tecumseh died with few to mourn, with fewer still to see him returned to the earth. And for a time, quite naturally, his name was hated by the whites. It was a name accursed, the name of a terrible enemy.

Yet the turning of the earth and the changing of the seasons also changed the memory of this warrior from the Ohio country. True, his dream had been broken, and denied his leadership the Indians of the northwestern frontier were forever broken themselves, destined to be so much baggage gathered up by the whites and shipped westward ahead of the restless tide of pioneer expansion.

In 1837 the Prophet, old and senile, his brain filled with half-remembered visions of his power, died on the alien ground of Kansas, prattling of his past.

But in the years when the wounds of the War of 1812 were healing, Tecumseh the enemy slowly died in the minds of Americans, and a new Tecumseh took his place in the history of the country—a Tecumseh honored for his greatness.

He even filled, at last, the unlikely role of unofficial patron saint for the midshipmen at the United States Naval Academy at Annapolis. The bronze statue of the Shawnee, put up in 1903 to replace a wooden statue of an obscure Delaware chief, was not the first honor the Navy paid Tecumseh . . . for a Union monitor named *Tecumseh* played an important role in the Battle of Mobile Bay during the Civil War, symbolically demonstrating that the American people saw Tecumseh's life in true perspective.

No Indian before him, and not an Indian after, ever dreamed a dream like that of Tecumseh. No other Indian, not even the Mohawk Brant, ever dreamed of gathering all the tribes of the explored North American continent into his hands and uniting them into one great force. None before and none after was ever touched with that greatness which serves as Tecumseh's monument.

This was dimly felt even in the years after the War of 1812, as the new Tecumseh began to be recognized by the American people.

Though he fought against the Americans and died at their hands, he was still an American hero, a wilderness giant, a man with the same praiseworthy traits that marked the pioneers who marched into his land and drove him to fight. He was a reasonable and fair man, hotly patriotic, fiercely loyal to his people, and he set an example for honesty, for plain speaking, for generosity and humane behavior never equaled by any other North American Indian.

Enemy of Americans . . . but a noble American.

In history's record it is no paradox. In history's record is eternally written the magnificence of Tecumseh of the Shawnee.

BIBLIOGRAPHY

Adams, Randolph Greenfield, *Lexington to Fallen Timbers,* University of Michigan, Ann Arbor, 1942.

Alvord, Clarence Walworth, *The Illinois Country,* 1673-1818, Illinois Centennial Commission, Springfield, 1920.

Beckwith, Hiram, *The Fort Wayne Manuscript,* Fergus Historical Series No. 26, Chicago, 1883.

Brackenridge, Henry, *History of the Late War Between the United States and Great Britain,* J. Cushing & Jewitt, Baltimore, 1817.

Brown, Samuel R., *View of the Campaigns of the North-Western Army,* F. Adancourt, Troy, 1814.

Campbell, Marion, *The Boyhood of Tecumseh,* Dorrance and Company, Philadelphia, 1940.

Cleaves, Freeman, *Old Tippecanoe: William Henry Harrison and His Time,* Charles Scribner's Sons, New York, 1939.

Collier, John, *Indians of the Americas,* W. W. Norton, New York, 1947.

Drake, Benjamin, *The Life of Tecumseh and His Brother the Prophet,* H. S. & J. Applegate & Co., Cincinnati, 1852.

Esarey, Logan, *History of Indiana from its Exploration to 1922,* Dayton Historical Publishing Co., Dayton, 1923.

Galloway, William A., *Old Chillicothe; Shawnee and Pioneer History,* The Buckeye Press, Xenia, 1934.

Goebel, Dorothy, *William Henry Harrison; A Political Biography,* Historical Bureau of the Indiana Library and Historical Department, Indianapolis, 1926.

Green, James A., *William Henry Harrison, His Life and Times,* Garrett & Massie, Richmond, 1941.

Gurd, Norman S., *The Story of Tecumseh,* W. Briggs, Toronto, 1912.

Harvey, Henry, *History of the Shawnee Indians from 1681 to 1854,* Cincinnati, 1855.

Hull, William, *Memoirs of the Campaign of the North-Western Army of the United States,* A.D. 1812, True & Greene, Boston, 1824.

Jackson, Isaac R., *Life of William Henry Harrison,* W. Marshall & Co., Philadelphia, 1840.

Jenkins, John S., *Jackson and the Generals of the War of 1812,* Philadelphia, 1856.

Johnston, John, *Vocabulary of the Language of the Shawaneese,* Archives of Americana, 1820.

Lessing, Benson J., *The Pictorial Field Book of the War of 1812,* New York, 1869.

Lucas, C. P., *The Canadian War of 1812,* The Clarendon Press, Oxford, 1906.

MacLeod, William Christie, *The American Indian Frontier,* Alfred A. Knopf, Inc., New York, 1928.

Moore, Edward E., *A Century of Indiana,* American Book Co., New York, 1910.

Nursey, Walter R., *The Story of Isaac Brock: Hero, Defender and Savior of Upper Canada, 1812,* A. C. McClurg & Co., Chicago, 1903.

Oskison, John M., *Tecumseh and his Times,* G. P. Putnam's Sons, New York, 1938.

Raymond, Ethel T., *Tecumseh,* Glasgow, Brook & Co., Toronto, 1951.

Sanders, Daniel C., *History of the Indian Wars,* E. Scrantom, Rochester, 1828.

Slocum, Charles E., *The Ohio Country Between the Years 1783 and 1815,* G. P. Putman's Sons, New York, 1910.

Smith, H. M., *Historical Sketches of Old Vincennes,* Vincennes, 1902.

Starkey, Marion L., *The Cherokee Nation, Alfred A. Knopf, Inc.,* New York, 1946.

Tucker, Glenn, *Poltroons and Patriots,* Bobbs-Merrill Co., Indianapolis, 1956.

——— *Tecumseh, Vision of Glory,* Bobbs-Merrill Co., Indianapolis, 1956.

Wilson, William E., *Shooting Star—The Story of Tecumseh,* Farrar & Rinehart, New York, 1942.

——— *The Wabash,* New York, 1940.

Writer's Program, Work Projects Administration, *Michigan,* New York, 1941; *Indiana,* New York, 1941; *Ohio,* New York, 1940.

Young, Colonel Bennett H., *The Battle of the Thames,* Filson Club Publication No. 18, Louisville, 1903.

INDEX